ELECTRO

Other Titles of Interest

ELECTRONIC BOARD GAMES

by

ROY BEBBINGTON

**BERNARD BABANI (publishing) LTD
THE GRAMPIANS
SHEPHERDS BUSH ROAD
LONDON W6 7NF
ENGLAND**

Please Note

Although every care has been taken with the production of this book to ensure that any projects, designs, modifications and/or programs, etc., contained herewith, operate in a correct and safe manner and also that all components specified are normally available in Great Britain, the Publishers and Author do not accept responsibility in any way for the failure, including fault in design, of any project, design, modification or program to work correctly or to cause damage to any other equipment that it may be connected to or used in conjunction with, or in respect of any other damage or injury that may be so caused, nor do the Publishers accept responsibility in any way for the failure to obtain specified components.

Notice is also given that if equipment that is still under warranty is modified in any way or used or connected with home-built equipment then that warranty may be void.

First Published — March 1994

British Library Cataloguing in Publication Data

Bebbington, R.
Electronic Board Games
I. Title
794.8

ISBN 0 85934 350 2

Printed and Bound in Great Britain by Cox & Wyman Ltd, Reading

Preface

A decided advantage of board games over computer games is that several players can easily participate. Not all members of the family are computer buffs, and a colourful board game with interesting accessories still has considerable appeal. Besides the thrill and enjoyment of playing a game with others, group involvement means that social skills are often enhanced.

Board games come in all shapes and sizes, but often fall into one of three categories: race games, games of strategy and card games.

While some games are designed merely for entertainment, there is a growing tendency these days to market games that also have educational value. The following games are a mixture of both. Most of them are new, while a few are updated versions of familiar games that have provided many hours of entertainment for past generations.

Although all the games have an electronics flavour, it is worth knowing that many of them can be made, and played, without recourse to the electronic circuits. For example, where moves are determined by an electronic dice or counter, conventional dice or spinners can be substituted. Also, where circuitry controls hazards or advantage moves, as in familiar board games, a pile of cards can be used instead.

If you are a beginner in electronics, it would be advisable to start with one of the simpler game projects. For instance, the treasure detector used in the Buried Treasure chapter, which is simply a series electrical circuit of an LED, a battery and a reed switch.

Games like Minefields and Pit-stop are more complicated, but the counter circuit is standardised, with slight differences, for several of the games. Generally, the main difference is the location of the counter light-emitting diodes (LEDs) around the various boards for the games. It would be advisable to bring these out on a terminal block for easy changeover unless the circuit is going to be permanent. There is ample variety in the following twenty chapters, with a hint or two of further suggestions to stretch the imagination.

Roy Bebbington

Contents

Chapter 1

ANTICIPATION

You can anticipate getting your number in this game if you're quick on the button. Although not the easiest circuit to tackle, this is a good one to build because it can be used in any of the other games in the book that need a dice or a decade counter. Apart from checking your reactions, this game tests your co-ordination and anticipation in pressing the FREEZE button for the number you desire.

Basically it consists of ten light-emitting diodes (LEDs) that flash continuously in sequence at a selected speed. The sequence can be stopped to display any one of the LEDs by pressing the FREEZE pushbutton at the right moment. The aim is to push the FREEZE button during the precise time that the required LED is lit. A target LED must be chosen and the SPEED control set before each round. For young children, or for starters, the SPEED control can be set for a fairly slow speed. Points can be awarded or subtracted depending how near a player gets to the target LED. For instance, if LED 1 is the target LED, then the scores could be 1 to 10, the lowest scorer after a fixed number of games being the winner. Alternatively, the first to score 100 is the loser, again the player with the lowest score being the winner. If you prefer to have the highest scorer the winner, then go for a 100 up, each player aiming for the highest number each turn. Turn the SPEED control up for an advanced game — further still for a random game.

When switched to DICE, only the first six LEDs light in sequence. Generally, the fast speed, giving random selection by the FREEZE button is used for most games, but an element of skill and interest is added to some games if players can regulate the score by anticipation. Often there are young children who love to join in. Selecting a suitable slower speed could be the solution.

A variation of the circuit is to omit LEDs 7 to 10. This will leave a break after LED 6 during which no LEDs are lit. After this, the cycle will resume and LEDs 1 to 6 will light.

1

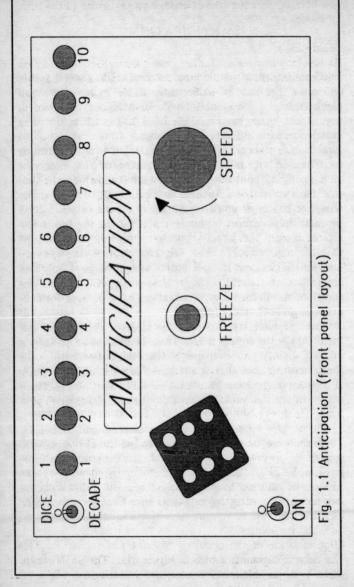

Fig. 1.1 Anticipation (front panel layout)

The break makes the task of choosing a particular LED a little bit harder.

Construction

As this may be used with other games, a compact construction is recommended. A plastic project box about 6 × 4 × 2 inches will allow the row of ten counter LEDs to be seen by all competitors. A suggested front panel layout is shown in Figure 1.1. Holes must be drilled for the ten LEDs, the three switches and the SPEED potentiometer.

Copper stripboard (0.1 inch matrix) 24 × 15 hole, is recommended to match the pin spacing of the integrated circuits. The layout of the components is shown on the top-side diagram of the stripboard in Figure 1.2. If you suffer from eye-strain, or you are a bit heavy on the solder, a good tip is to splay alternate pins of the ICs along the top of the printed circuit board (pcb), instead of feeding them through to the copper track. This virtually doubles the distance between tracks, and is most useful when you have only one connection to the pin, as in the case of the IC2 outputs. In addition, the unused copper track can now be used for connections on both sides of the IC.

The underside layout shows the soldered connections and the breaks in the copper strips. These breaks can be made by a drill of slightly greater diameter than the copper strip, or a special cutting tool that is advertised in most of the popular electronics magazines. Care must be taken that no breaks are forgotten and that no whiskers of copper are missed that could introduce short-circuits.

The topside layout shows the components and wire links. These links can be made with single strand tinned copper wire if there is no possibility of short-circuits; otherwise use insulated wire. For clarity, the flexible insulated wires to the LEDs and switches have not been included. However, the relevant stripboard soldering points have been given on these components.

Circuit

The circuit diagram is shown in Figure 1.3. The 555 timer is wired as an astable multivibrator, the operating frequency of

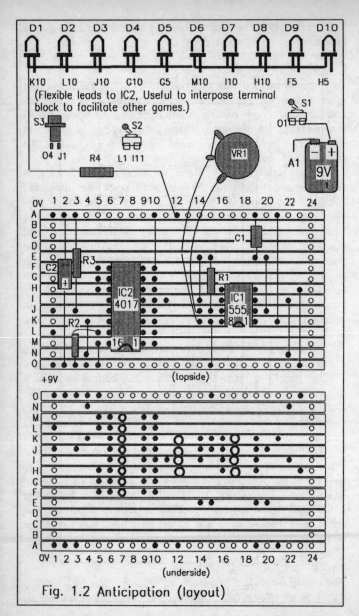

Fig. 1.2 Anticipation (layout)

4

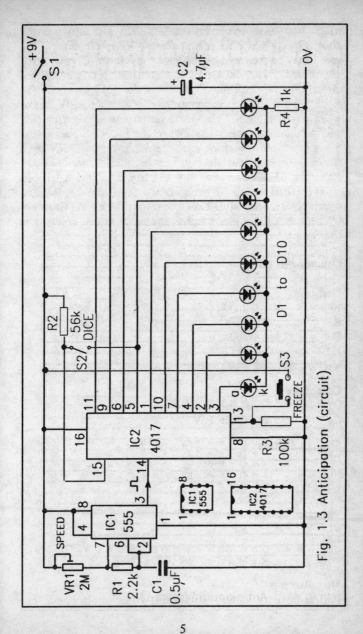

Fig. 1.3 Anticipation (circuit)

5

which can be controlled from less than 1Hz up to about 200Hz by the SPEED potentiometer VR1. If desired, the speed may be increased by reducing the value of C1, say to 0.2 microfarad. The output of the multivibrator is connected directly to the clock input, pin 14 of the 4017 counter. The clock enable, pin 13, is connected via R3 to the 0V line so when power is applied via S1, the outputs go high sequentially and the flashing cycle starts. When the FREEZE pushbutton S3 is depressed the clock enable pin is taken high and holds the sequence in the state it was in when 'frozen' by S3. Releasing S3 allows the cycling to carry on where it left off.

The DICE switch S2 connects the reset, pin 15, to pin 5 which gives a reset after LED 6 to restart the cycle. Capacitor C2 acts as a decoupler to prevent any unwanted coupling in the circuit.

Components List

Resistors
R1	2.2kΩ
R2	56kΩ
R3	100kΩ
R4	1kΩ
VR1	2MΩ carbon

Capacitors
C1	0.5μF
C2	4.7μF 10V

Semiconductors
IC1	555 timer
IC2	4017 decade divider
D1 – D10	LEDs

Switches
S1	S.P.S.T.
S2	S.P.S.T.
S3	push-to-make (non-locking)

Miscellaneous
Project box, 9V battery, stripboard, wiring, control knob, etc.

Chapter 2

TRADING PLACES

Trading Places is a good example of a game that makes full use of the Anticipation circuit described in the first chapter. All three switch facilities are employed, the SPEED switch, the DICE and DECADE switches. The idea is to collect all commodities listed on a chosen card from the various trading places on the map as you move around. Your move is decided by the electronic counter, which can be switched either to DICE or DECADE depending which is more advantageous. For example, if you require a commodity that is six moves away or less, it is better to use the dice mode. Conversely if you need to travel a long distance to the next commodity, it pays to use the decade mode. It also makes things easier if the SPEED control is reduced, but this should be decided by mutual consent. Slow it down if young children are playing.

Rules of Play

Up to four players are able to play Trading Places.

Each player can start wherever he or she likes on the map and puts a counter down to indicate this. A 'Bill of Lading' card (a kind of shopping list) is then turned face up from a small pack, which lists the commodities that are needed for the consignment. After deciding who goes first by the decade counter, the players move in sequence using the decade or dice mode. The first player to collect all commodities listed is the winner. The commodities to collect can be small pieces of card with the name written on, or suitable pictures, or even plastic shapes where appropriate. These could be housed in a shallow tray. Commodities could be traded for by agreement, for instance, when one trader has collected more than one on his travels.

Construction

You will need the electronic counter from the Anticipation circuit, although you could manage with a humble dice (or die to be correct). The map needs to be fairly large to allow

Fig. 2.1 Trading places (board layout)

plenty of room for the counters, and stuck on to stout cardboard. The map shown happens to be of England, Scotland and Wales, but it could easily be Australia where you deliver the goods. The map on Figure 2.1 can be photocopied and enlarged, or you may have a spare map that can be used.

Several Bill of Lading cards can be made out with say, half a dozen commodities on each. For example: cotton, electronics, ships, coal, wool, iron. An ideal choice if you started in Manchester.

A harder game will include one of the single commodities, for instance carpets; everyone will have to trek to Axminster for one of these. Information on the various places can be included in the game to add interest.

Chapter 3

BURIED TREASURE

Searching for treasure is always exciting, whether it's on a sandy beach, on an ancient Roman site, or in your back garden. This particular board game chooses the traditional desert island to look for buried gold. The size of the board is immaterial, but obviously the larger it is, the harder it is to find the treasure with an electronic detector. For a party, or social evening, a large table-size or floor map with one or more detectors could prove interesting and amusing.

Basically, we have a picture board of a desert island with several small magnets hidden under the board in strategic places as listed in the chart. These hidden 'treasure chests' can be located by a hand-held electronic treasure detector consisting of a series circuit containing an LED indicator, a battery and a reed switch. When the reed switch is close to a magnet it is actuated and brings on the LED. If the scoring depends on the number of turns that are taken to find the treasure, then, for each turn, the detector must be placed directly on the suspected spot rather than moved around the suspected area. However, if scoring is on a time basis, then combing the area is allowed. The latter method of scoring is better for a large board where pin-pointing the magnets is more difficult.

A typical map is shown in Figure 3.1, but I'm sure your artistic flair can improve on this.

Treasure Charts
Treasure charts are reputably old documents that have been found that give instructions as to where the treasure is to be located. Only one complies with the magnets that have been set up in the board. One person, Chaptain Hornblower, is delegated to set up the magnets according to the relevant treasure chart, also to act as scorer and see fair play. Several treasure charts will need to be made up (see Figure 3.2) otherwise the brighter contestants will soon cotton on to where the treasure lies if the game is played often. Two charts,

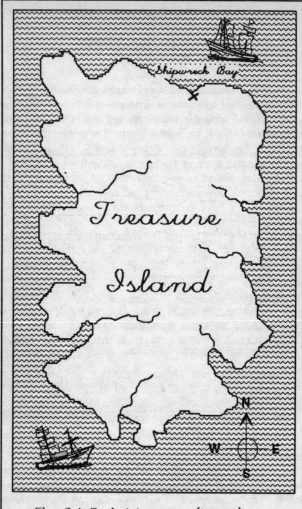

Fig. 3.1 Buried treasure (layout)

12

The island is 8 miles East to West
and 12 miles North to South.

We landed at Shipwreck Bay and
buried the first treasure 2 miles due South.
From there we set our compass SW and
walked almost one and a half
miles before we buried the next chest.

The third treasure chest lies 3 miles South.
The fourth chest lies 4 miles SW.

We went ashore at Shipwreck Bay and travelled
2 miles due West before burying the first chest.
We then struck due South for 2 miles
before burying the second chest.

The third chest lies 2 miles due West,
and the fourth chest at the source of a
river flowing from the South shores of
the island.

Examples of two charts that can be prepared
according to the positions of the magnets.
The first chart set-up is illustrated in
the pegboard layout of Figure 3.4.

Other charts can be set up by measuring
distances on the pegboard or if using
the disc method, by finding the points
with the detector, marking each turn of
the disc.

Fig. 3.2 Buried treasure (charts)

or more, can also be offered by Captain Hornblower to the contestant who first has to determine, by trying some of the clues, which chart is authentic. Once a treasure chest is located, the contestant will know which chart to use, and the rest of the treasure chests should be easily found. All false clues (LED not lit) tried before deciding which is the right chart, mean more turns or more time.

If the same treasure chart arrangement is to be used for all contestants, then they need to be banished from the Treasure Island before play and called in one by one for their turns.

Construction

(a) Board

A suitable size is 12in × 10in. The map shown in Figure 3.1 is easy to arrange as already mentioned. It can be drawn on yellow or green card with a blue sea in the background or whatever takes your fancy. The main problem is locating the magnets behind so that the game does not become predictable. Here's how the prototype, Figure 3.3, worked. A cardboard disc, the size of the island was fastened to the rear of it by a paper fastener centrally mounted. Several small bar magnets were attached to the disc by tape, spaced at intervals. Numbers written on the periphery of the disc were then turned to a reference line on the rear of the map to indicate to the person setting-up the turn which chart is to be used. Beforehand, the instructions on that chart were written to conform with the magnet positions on the front of the map. The disc must be rotated to line-up the next chart number to write up the next clues for the magnet positions, and so on. When rotated, a magnet may lie under the sea: no problem, the clue on the chart could locate the treasure in 15 fathoms a mile off the SW point. Before start of play, unseen, Captain Hornblower selects the chart he is going to use and rotates the disc to the number allocated to that chart. He then offers this authentic chart and one or more others to the contestant.

Although rotating the magnet pattern, it is still restrictive. An alternative shown in Figure 3.4 uses peg-board for the board with a matrix of holes at 1 inch spacing. A thin card can be pasted on top of it for the picture board. Several small

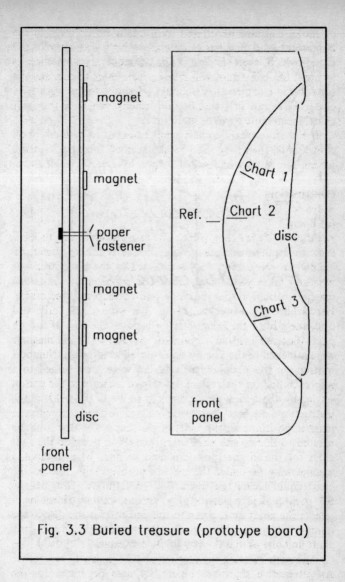

Fig. 3.3 Buried treasure (prototype board)

15

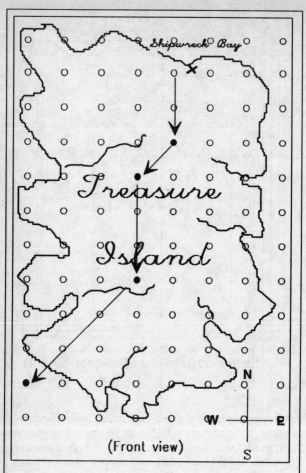

Shipwreck Bay

Treasure

Island

N
W   E
S

(Front view)

Magnet set-up of Chart 1 (see Fig. 3.2)

Fig. 3.4   Buried treasure (pegboard layout)

16

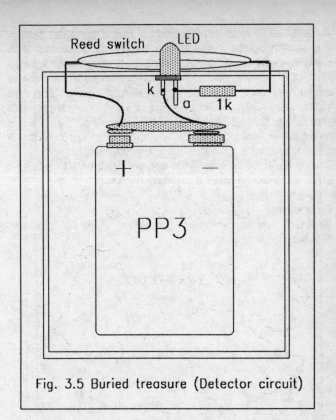

Fig. 3.5 Buried treasure (Detector circuit)

cylindrical magnets are plugged into holes, and moved around as required to produce the different charts. The matrix of holes allows for accurate bearings for the treasure chests.

For table-top or floor maps, corrugated cardboard can be used with the magnets in the corrugations. Alternatively, the magnets can be sandwiched between two layers of cardboard. Construction is made easier because this is one of the few games where there are no electronics below board.

(b) Treasure Detector
The size of the detector depends on how small a box can hold a PP3 battery. A potting box, or a small project box may be

available. The main consideration is that it has a flat surface that can sit on the map with the reed switch in contact with the map surface. A typical construction using an ABS/T3 by Marco (72 × 46 × 22mm) is shown together with the detector circuit in Figure 3.5. The circuit is very simple. The reed switch is mounted on the outside of the box, with the leads protruding through holes into the lower side. The LED is mounted on the side of the box above the reed switch. A limiting resistor is connected in series with the LED.

For the floor version of the treasure detector, a long handle attachment would make it easier on the knees.

Components
Pegboard and/or cardboard, ABS box, LED, 1kΩ resistor, PP3 battery, wiring, etc.

Chapter 4

MINEFIELDS

Navigate your two ships through magnetic minefields — first into port wins! The board layout is shown in Figure 4.1 and the circuit in Figure 4.2.

The game can be played by up to four players, each with two ships. In turn, under electronic control, the ships are

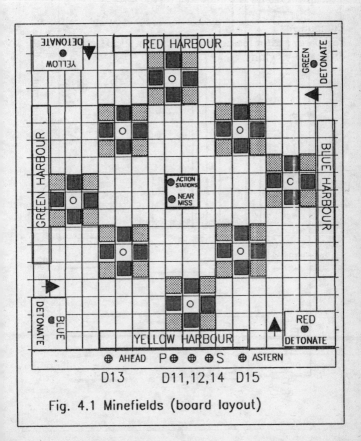

Fig. 4.1 Minefields (board layout)

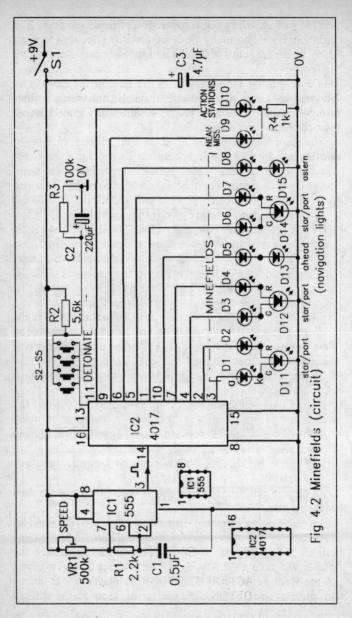

Fig 4.2 Minefields (circuit)

20

steered past minefields in the direction of the home port. The eight minefields normally flash sequentially (free-run) to warn ships of danger, until a mine is detonated (glows steadily) by a player.

Depending on temperament or the state of the race, some players may take the longer safe channels (unless under other orders), while others may risk a winning dash for the home harbour via the minefields.

Movement

Players move in turn by pressing their DETONATE push-button, which freezes the flashing minefield display for a few seconds. This results in one of two situations, as follows:

1. On detonate, one of the eight mines will glow for a few seconds together with one of the navigation lights. The player will observe which of the navigation lights is on, and also check if there is a ship lying on one of the eight shaded squares that surround the glowing mine. After the player has made his move, any victim in the minefield must either return his ship to base in the case of a direct hit (dark square) or take a NEAR MISS card (light square) and act upon instructions.

With regard to the direction of play, Figure 4.3 shows the four moves. These are made in relation to a player's starting direction shown next to the DETONATE button:

* A green (starboard) light indicates a forward diagonal turn to the right.
* A red (port) light indicates a forward diagonal turn to the left.
* AHEAD indicates a forward move directly towards the harbour.
* ASTERN indicates a backwards move directly towards the base.

A ship is only moved one square at a time, unless a card instructs otherwise.

2. If a mine does not remain on after a 'DETONATE', then one of the two centre LEDs ACTION STATIONS or NEAR MISS will glow. If it is a NEAR MISS light, then the player will take a NEAR MISS card and act on it. However, in the event of ACTION STATIONS, all players are at liberty to press their DETONATE button as soon as the display

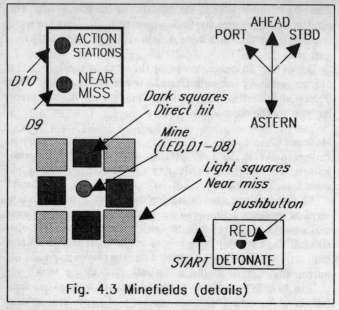

Fig. 4.3 Minefields (details)

returns to free-run, primarily to ward off any danger or to create havoc. The player will then take a card from the **ACTION STATIONS** pile and act on the instructions. Cards can sometimes be held for future use if not valid. In this case, they will take the place of a turn. After use they will be returned to the bottom of the pile.

The SPEED control VR1 can be panel-mounted if desired and marked 'half-speed' and 'full-speed' to cater for younger children, and for special instructions, e.g. on **ACTION STATION** cards.

Depending on the agreed speed and a certain amount of anticipation, the display can easily be frozen on a desired mine, or navigation direction to shorten a game.

If a move cannot be made for any reason, e.g. obstacles such as coast lines, other ships, mines, then the move is forfeited. A move can be made by either of a player's two ships when thought advantageous, e.g. to hold direction or to avoid a minefield.

NOTE: Ships cannot be moved sideways.

Hazards

One of the eight mines can be detonated (permanently lit): by a player's 'DETONATE' switch as a normal turn, by detonating after the ACTION STATION light comes on, or if an ACTION STATION card says DETONATE.

Any ships in a minefield when it is detonated (one mine permanently on) take instructions from the top 'NEAR MISS' card if in the light-shaded square, or if a 'DIRECT HIT' is registered (on a dark square) go back to base for repairs.

Some ideas for the NEAR MISS and ACTION STATION cards are shown on Figure 4.4, but you will no doubt think of others along these lines for creating problems, e.g. engine trouble, collision, fog in channel, mines adrift, etc.

The 'HALF SPEED AND DETONATE' card introduces an element of skill. It allows more time for a player to anticipate which mine shall be detonated. The player operates the 'HALF SPEED' button to slow down the display before detonating. This gives a chance to inflict a direct hit or a near miss on any rival ships already in a minefield.

The 'SPEED' control can be reduced for the first few games, or to assist younger players; alternatively, younger players could use the 'HALF SPEED' control for each move.

Ships may not enter an opponent's HARBOUR.

Circuit

The circuit is similar to that described in the Anticipation circuit of Chapter 1. The 555 timer can be varied by VR1 to give a suitable speed for the free-run display for the mine and navigational LEDs. The dice facility is not used, but an unusual feature is the inclusion of three tricolour LEDs in series with the minefield LEDs to give green (starboard) and red (port) navigation signals. Also, the electrolytic C2 together with R3, 100kΩ, provides a time constant to hold the detonate and navigation information for a few seconds for scrutiny after a DETONATE pushbutton is released. This time can be lengthened or shortened as desired by altering the value of C2 (reduce value to shorten and vice versa).

The layout is very similar to that of Figure 1.3, except for the extra LEDs, C2 and R3.

NEAR MISS!

Propellor damaged. Drop anchor for one turn.

NEAR MISS!

Turn to port to avoid collision.

NEAR MISS!

Avoiding action. Double next move.

NEAR MISS!

Mines adrift. Next move at half speed.

ACTION STATIONS!

Ship holed. Miss two turns for repairs.

ACTION STATIONS!

Night manoeuvres. Turn to port next two moves.

ACTION STATIONS!

Thick fog in channel. Drop anchor for two turns.

ACTION STATIONS!

Debris ahead, go astern two places.

ACTION STATIONS!

Superstructure damaged by fire. Miss three turns to fight fire.

NEAR MISS!

Engines overhauled. Stop one turn to pick up spares.

Fig. 4.4 Minefields (sample cards)

Components

Resistors
R1	2.2kΩ
R2	5.6kΩ
R3	100kΩ
R4	1kΩ

Potentiometers
VR1	500kΩ potentiometer

Capacitors
C1	0.5μF
C2	220μF elect. 10V
C3	4.7μF elect. 10V

Semiconductors
IC1	NE555CP timer
IC2	CD4017 CMOS decade counter/divider
D1 – D8	LEDs (red) TIL20
D9	LED (orange) TIL 20
D10	LED (red) TIL20
D11, 12, 14	LED (tricolour green/red)
D13	LED (yellow) TIL20
D15	LED (orange) TIL20

Switches
S1	S.P.S.T. (ON/OFF)
S2 – S5	pushbutton, non-locking (DETONATE)

Miscellaneous
Shallow box, 9V PP3 battery, plastic shapes for ships, strip-board, wiring, etc.

Chapter 5

HEADS/TAILS

It may seem a little extravagant to have a heads or tails simulator, when it is easy enough to toss a coin to make a decision. However, an electronic version does not get lost in the grass, roll off the table, have two heads or two tails. Moreover, if you have already built the Anticipation circuit of Chapter 1 you can easily adapt it for Heads/Tails with four extra components.

You can of course build a heads/tails circuit with an oscillator controlling a bistable, but as we have already familiarised ourselves with the 4017 it seems logical to adapt the carry out, pin 12, for this purpose. As this is a divide by ten output, it is necessary to speed up the 555 frequency otherwise it will be easy to anticipate the heads or tails LEDs; slowing down the SPEED potentiometer VR1 can introduce another game of skill.

Circuit

You will notice that the SPEED control VR1 has been reduced in value because generally a higher rate of flashing between the two LEDs is required. The output pulses from IC1, pin 3 are fed directly to pin 14, the input of the decade counter IC2. It is possible to make use of the ten output pins of the decade counter, but for the purpose of the heads/tails simulator only the carry out (pin 12) is used. The two LEDs D1 and D2 are series connected across the 9-volt supply and would both be on permanently if the current-limiting resistors R3 and R4 were not fitted. The alternate high and low pulses on pin 12 cause D1 and D2 to light sequentially until the FREEZE button S2 is pressed. Clock enable Pin 13 is normally pulled low via R2 and counting is enabled. However, the clock enable goes high when S2 is pressed, the clock signal is blocked and holds the counter in whatever state it was the instant S2 was closed.

Two different colours are used for the LEDs so that heads or tails is easily distinguished. A suggestion for a front panel

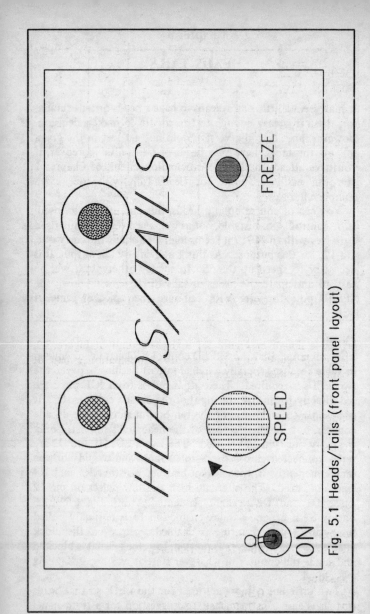

Fig. 5.1 Heads/Tails (front panel layout)

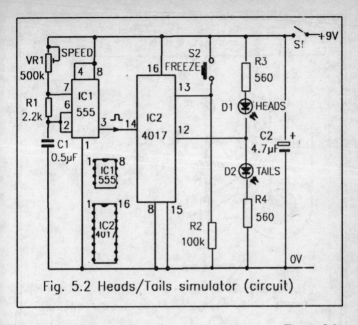

Fig. 5.2 Heads/Tails simulator (circuit)

layout is shown in Figure 5.1 and the circuit in Figure 5.2. Figure 5.3 shows how to adapt the Anticipation circuit of Chapter 1, as mentioned earlier.

Components

Resistors
R1   2.2kΩ
R2   100kΩ
R3   560Ω
R4   560Ω

Potentiometers
VR1   500kΩ potentiometer

Capacitors
C1   0.5µF
C2   4.7µF elect. 10V

29

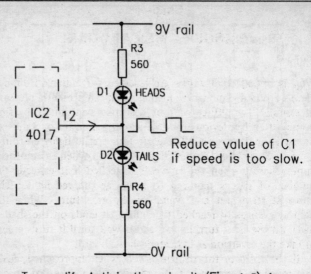

To modify Anticipation circuit (Fig. 1.3) for heads/tails facility, add above components.

Fig. 5.3 Heads/Tails (mod. to Fig. 1.3)

Semiconductors

IC1	NE555CP timer
IC2	CD4017 CMOS decade counter/divider
D1	TIL20 LED (yellow)
D2	TIL20 LED (red)

Switches

S1	S.P.S.T.
S2	pushbutton, non-locking

Miscellaneous

Project box, 9V battery, stripboard, wiring, control knob, etc.

Chapter 6

DANGER – MEN AT WORK!

Why is it that road works are reserved for a Bank Holiday? Here's a board game where men at work can present a pleasant diversion! Two, three or four motorists can aim to be first home, often by devious routes. Either a counter or a die can be used for the moves. There are four traffic lights en route.

If the first or second light is red, when a motorist approaches it, then the move is cancelled if it exceeds the number of spaces required to arrive at the red light. The motorist stays put and waits for the next turn. When the light is eventually reached (the motorist lands on the shaded pad), on the next turn he can either wait until it turns green, or take the diversion as indicated on the board.

If the third or fourth light is red, when approached, again the move is cancelled if it exceeds the number of spaces required to arrive at the red light. Finally, when the light is reached by selecting, or shaking, the right number, a 'C' prompts the motorist to take a 'Control Card'. This will generally give the opportunity to move the 'Traffic Light' switch, which hopefully will change the light to green (and possibly some of the others to red or green). If a motorist cannot move, he remains on the 'C' space, using up Control Cards each turn until he can go. Other 'C' spaces occur around the routes to aid or frustrate motorists.

'Men at Work Cards' must be taken and acted upon when you land on a space where the man is 'attempting to open an umbrella!'. Motorists must arrive home by the correct number of moves – no breaking down the back of the garage!

Construction
The playing board can be about 10in by 15in. The prototype was 3-ply, but thick card or hardboard could be used if to hand, the board layout is shown in Figure 6.1. The road network was drawn on thin white card and fitted over the plywood. There is plenty of scope for a colourful, attractive board using plenty of imagination. Once the layout is

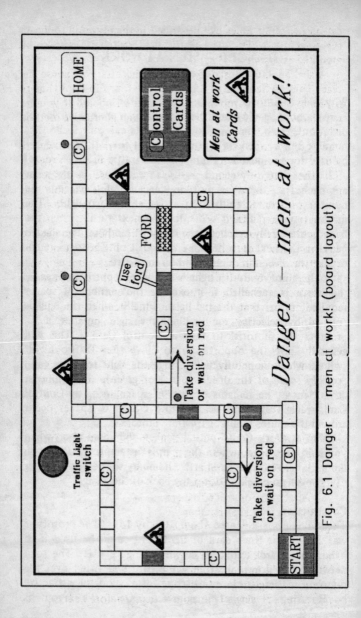

Fig. 6.1 Danger – men at work! (board layout)

established, four holes can be drilled in the plywood to locate the tri-colour LEDs. The traffic light switch S2 can also be mounted as shown.

A shallow box construction will be necessary to house the rear of the switch and the circuits. The four flip-flops (Figure 6.2) may easily be mounted on copper stripboard if you are familiar with this form of layout, if not an alternative method of construction is suggested later.

Figure 6.3 shows the wiring layout. The transistor bases are separately connected to the single-pole 12-way rotary switch S2. There are only eight bases, so four of these are connected to the extra four contacts. If an 8-way switch is available, this can be used for S2. Rotating S2 switches the flip-flop bases, and in turn the LEDs.

For the beginner in electronics, and for those who need to work in plenty of space, the layout of Figure 6.4 may be attractive. The circuit is mounted on nine brass drawing pins affixed in plywood. It is recommended that the transistors are soldered last so that the legs are spared excessive heat.

The motors that 'hurtle' around the track can be shaped out of plastic or thick card in distinguishing colours.

Cards

All cards can be about 2in by 3in, preferably in two different colours, say red for the 'Men at Work' Cards and yellow for the 'Control' Cards. Cards should be facing down in a pile and replaced under the pile after use.

The Control Cards can state that the S2 switch is turned:
— clockwise by number of last move (or 1 if on 'C' space)
— anti-clockwise by number of last move (or 1 if on 'C' space)
— clockwise on to desired green
— anti-clockwise on to desired green
— clockwise by stated number
— anti-clockwise by stated number.

The Men at Work Cards can state:
— Road Works in progress, miss a turn
— Narrow bridge, miss a turn
— Road repairs, single lane, no overtaking before next

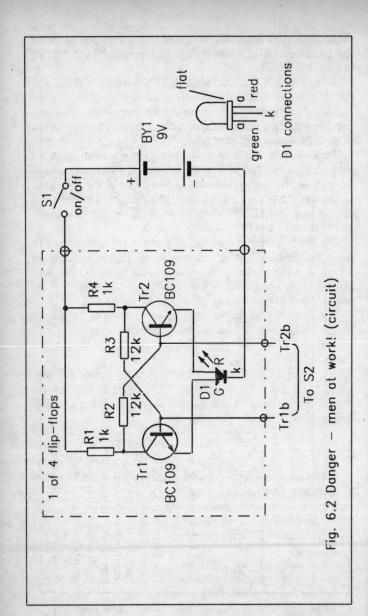

Fig. 6.2 Danger — men at work! (circuit)

34

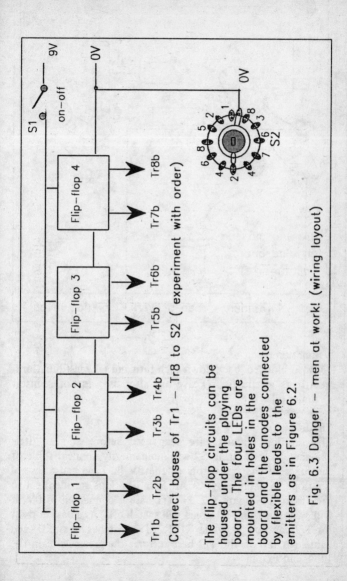

The flip-flop circuits can be housed under the playing board. The four LEDs are mounted in holes in the board and the anodes connected by flexible leads to the emitters as in Figure 6.2.

Connect bases of Tr1 – Tr8 to S2 (experiment with order)

Fig. 6.3 Danger – men at work! (wiring layout)

35

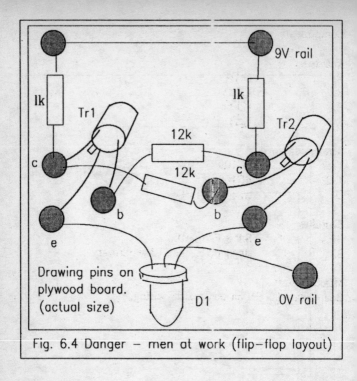

Fig. 6.4 Danger — men at work (flip—flop layout)

junction.
– Road blocked, back down each turn and take last junction.
  Affects all traffic. Leave out after use, do not re-insert
  under pile.

Circuit
The flip-flop circuits have been used before so need little
explanation. Rotating S2 will momentarily connect some of
the bases of the transistors to the 0V line and cause several
flip-flops to change over. All four flip-flops are identical to
the circuit of Figure 6.2. If Tr1 base is connected to 0V, it
will switch off and D1 green will switch off. As a base current
for Tr2 can now flow via R1, R2, Tr2 switches on and D1 red
lights. A 0V on the Tr2 base restores the green light on the
LED, and so on.

Components

Resistors
R1	1kΩ
R2	12kΩ
R3	12kΩ
R4	1kΩ

Semiconductors
Tr1	BC109
Tr2	BC109
D1	tri-colour LED

Switches
S1	S.P.S.T. on-off
S2	single-pole, 8- or 12-way rotary

Miscellaneous
Board material, 9V battery, cards, wiring, etc.

Chapter 7

GAME TIMER

Quite a few board games and card games call for a timer, although not always required by the rules. How often do you find a game tedious because someone takes an age to make a decision. This game timer will put a stop to that by setting a pre-determined time for a move. After that time has elapsed, a buzzer will sound, either disqualifying the player, or forcing him to make a decision. To cover a large timing interval, on one variable control, the time can be switched between seconds and minutes.

The circuit for this timer, Figure 7.1, is based on the ubiquitous NE555N integrated circuit, operating in its monostable mode, a suggested front panel is shown in Figure 7.2.

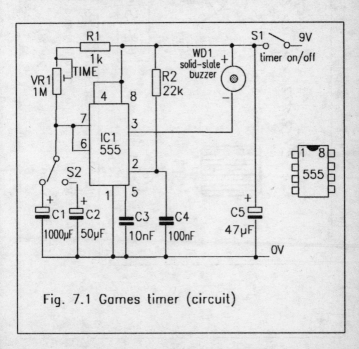

Fig. 7.1 Games timer (circuit)

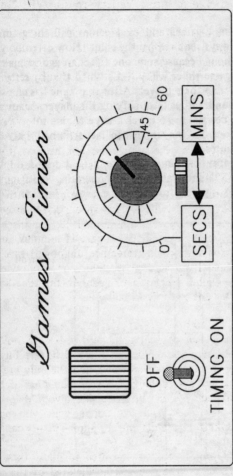

Fig. 7.2 Game timer (front panel)

Games Timer

OFF TIMING ON

SECS MINS

Calibrate scale according to requirements
against second or minute hand of clock.

The time delay depends on the charging of a capacitor through a resistor. Capacitor C2 is switched into circuit when the interval required is in seconds, and C1 is switched in when the interval required is in minutes. Variable resistor VR1 covers the two ranges.

The basic action is that the output pin 3, discharge pin 7 and threshold pin 6 are normally pulled low internally. At switch-on, the timing capacitor, C1 or C2, charges exponentially via VR1 and R1 from the 9V line. When the capacitor has charged to two-thirds the supply voltage, pins 3, 7 and 6 are pulled to zero and the solid-state buzzer connected between pin 3 and the +9V rail sounds.

The values of the timing components VR1 and C1/C2 can be chosen to suit your own requirements. For instance, if you want to obtain similar scales for seconds and minutes divide the value of the larger capacitor C1 by sixty to calculate the smaller one (approximately $16\mu F$). On experiment, with the $1000\mu F$ capacitor a fixed value of resistance $27k\Omega$ in place of VR1 gave a delay of about half a minute, $100k\Omega$ in place of VR1 gave a delay of 2 minutes, $560k\Omega$ gave 11 minutes, and a fixed resistance of 2 megohm (tolerance unknown) gave an elapsed time of nearly an hour. Use a clock or watch with a second hand or digital indication to calibrate the time scale when satisfied that the controls are suitable.

Construction

The circuit is built on a small stripboard (14 × 15 holes), matrix 0.1in to match the pinning of the 555 IC (see Figure 7.3). The components are not crowded, and the only breaks in the copper strips are the four between the pins of the integrated circuit, shown on the underside layout diagram. Make sure you leave no whiskers of copper when you make the break. Looking for faults due to short-circuits can be very time-consuming!

A small ABS project box can be used to house the few components. However, the size will be dictated by the size of the scale and how detailed you want the time graduations. A suitable layout for the front panel is shown. The solid-state buzzer can be mounted on the panel or behind it as preferred; make sure you observe the correct polarity.

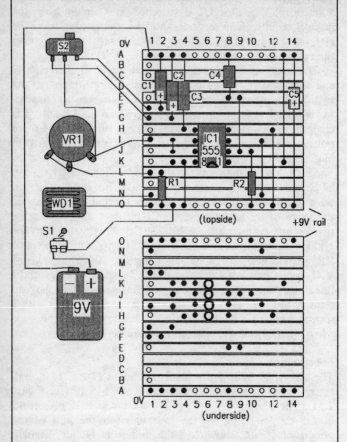

The layout of the components and connections shown on the topside of the stripboard. Notice the breaks to be made in the copper strip between the IC on the underside, and the soldering points.

Fig. 7.3 Games timer (layout)

Components

Resistors
R1 $1k\Omega$
R2 $22k\Omega$
VR1 $1M\Omega$ lin. (see text)

Capacitors
C1 $1000\mu F$ 16V (see text)
C2 $50\mu F$ 16V (see text)
C3   10nF plastic foil
C4   100nF plastic foil
C5 $47\mu F$ 16V

Semiconductors
IC1   NE555N
WD1   Solid-state buzzer

Switches
S1   S.P.S.T. (Timer on/off)
S2   slider, single-pole changeover

Miscellaneous
Project box, stripboard, 9 volt battery (PP3), wiring, etc.

Chapter 8

ELECTRONIC DICE

1. Dicey Reed Counter

This is the simplest electronic dice. It is an electro-mechanical device consisting of a spinner disc with a magnet attached that can activate one of six reed switches. Each reed switch is in series with an LED which indicates a number from 1 to 6. The reed switches are located radially and equidistantly behind the spinner as shown in Figure 8.1. Depending on the strength of the magnet and the distance between the reed switches, there may be blank spots, i.e. no reed switch is activated and consequently no LED lights. This is why I call

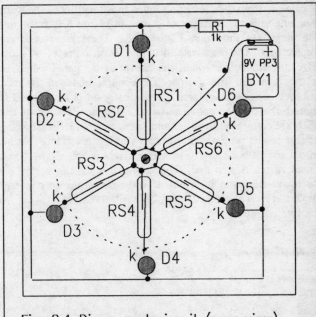

Fig. 8.1 Dicey reed circuit (rear view)

it a dicey reed counter. Fortunately, this is no problem. Another turn may be given if no LED lights, or this zero condition could be included as part of a game.

When the spinner disc is rotated the LEDs flash sequentially, slowing down as the disc slows down. This adds a measure of suspense as you wait for the final number to come up.

Construction

The spacing of the reed switches needs to be fairly accurate to give an even count. Use a protractor to ensure 60 degree spacing between them. The size of the spinner disc may be as large as desired provided the reed switches are close to the centre and the LEDs are located so they are not hidden by the spinner disc. The prototype spinner was about 4in diameter.

Mount the six reed switches radially on the rear of a sheet of Paxolin or plastic. Solder all inner ends together in the form of a ring around the pivot as shown in Figure 8.1, front and side views are shown in Figure 8.2. These inner ends are connected to the negative end of the 9-volt battery. A short 4BA nut and bolt through the centre of the panel will serve as the pivot for the spinner. The outer ends of the reed switches are each soldered to the cathode (k) of an LED around the periphery of the panel. The anode ends of the LEDs are connected together and are routed via a 1kΩ limiting resistor to the positive end of the 9-volt battery. Note that no on/off switch is necessary because current is only drawn when a reed switch is activated. The spinner disc has the magnet on the lower side, and is lifted off when not in use to conserve the battery. The magnet must be positioned correctly before it is finally fixed.

Components

Resistors

R1   1kΩ

Switches

RS1 − RS6   reed switches

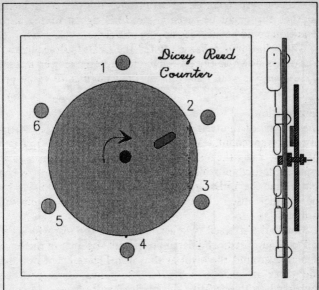

Fig. 8.2 Dicey reed (front and side views)

Semiconductors

D1 – D6   TIL20 LEDs

Miscellaneous

Paxolin panel and spinner disc, 9V battery, 4BA nut and bolt
for pivot, wiring, etc.

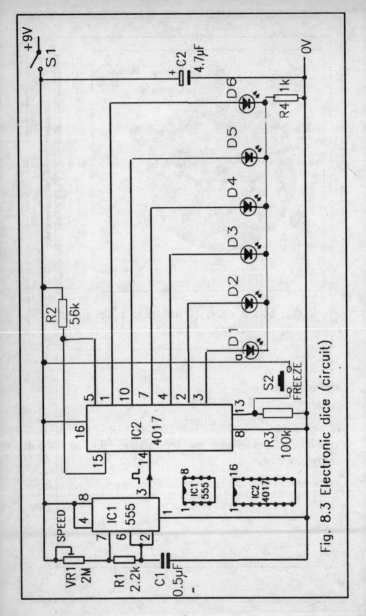

Fig. 8.3 Electronic dice (circuit)

48

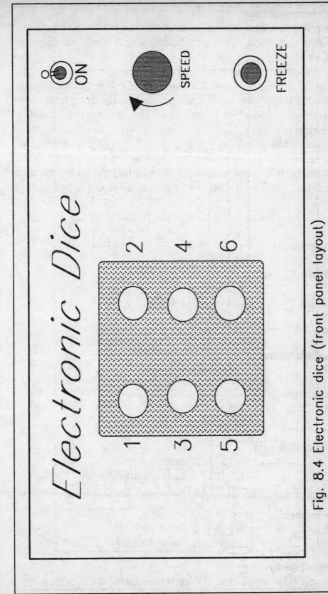

Fig. 8.4 Electronic dice (front panel layout)

49

2. Electronic Dice

An electronic dice is a useful asset for many other board games besides this book. It is particularly useful when travelling or where playing space is limited.

The circuit, Figure 8.3 is a simplified version of the Anticipation counter circuit of Chapter 1. Only six of the decade outputs have been used and pin 5 has to be permanently connected to the reset, pin 15. The rest of the circuit is identical to Figure 1.2.

The front panel layout, Figure 8.4, shows one method of mounting the LEDs within the outline of a dice (or die to be correct). It is possible to make the LEDs light up in true dice patterns, but the circuit is too complex for the scope of this book.

The layout can easily be adapted from Figure 1.3.

Components

Resistors

R1	2.2kΩ
R2	56kΩ
R3	100kΩ
R4	1kΩ

Potentiometers

VR1	2MΩ potentiometer

Capacitors

C1	0.5µF
C2	4.7µF elect. 10V

Semiconductors

IC1	NE555CP timer
IC2	CD4017 decade counter/divider
D1 – D6	TIL20 LEDs

Switches

S1	S.P.S.T.
S2	pushbutton (non-locking)

Miscellaneous

Project box, stripboard, 9V battery, control knob, wiring, etc.

Chapter 9

GIVE IT A WHIRL

There is a strange fascination about lights that slow down to decide a player's fate, as we observe from the antics, groans or cheers of TV audiences.

Here, the question is ' . . . what question are you going to get when you spin the wheel?' Give it a whirl and see! When the ten flashing lights around the wheel eventually slow down and stop, then the one that stays alight indicates one of ten subjects. Give the wheel another whirl and when it stops the number adjacent to the LED that is alight will indicate which question you have to answer on that subject. A repetitive sound from a solid-state buzzer accompanies the wheel rotation as the LEDs flash sequentially.

So there are ten subjects and ten questions on each subject. The quizmaster gives you 2 points for a correct answer or offers the question to your opponent if your answer is incorrect. If he or she answers correctly it earns them a point. The game can also be played by two teams, a player from each side spinning the wheel alternately.

Construction

The front panel shown in Figure 9.1 is about half-scale. However, if this quiz game is intended for social evenings a larger panel would be more suitable for a viewing audience. The small disc (wheel) carries a magnet and freely rotates on the rectangular panel. This has a reed switch affixed on the back. Figure 9.2 shows the mechanical arrangement and the panel connections. A small bolt and bush to which the wheel is attached passes through the panel and is secured by a washer and nut at the rear. The magnet is positioned to pass freely past the reed switch at each rotation of the wheel. The reed switch contacts are connected to the trigger input of circuit Figure 9.3. The LEDs D1 to D10 are mounted on the panel around the periphery of the wheel in numerical sequence. Extension leads from the stripboard are necessary. A shallow box arrangement is necessary to protect the below-panel

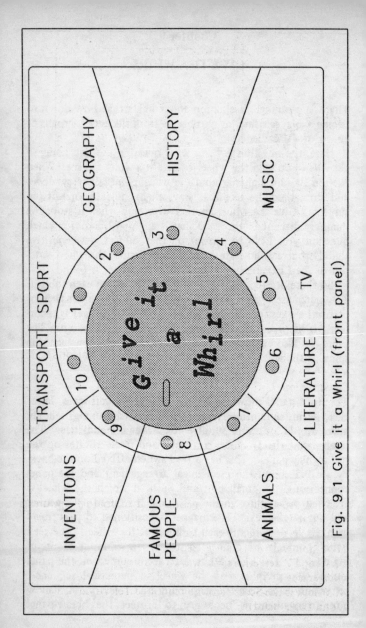

Fig. 9.1 Give it a Whirl (front panel)

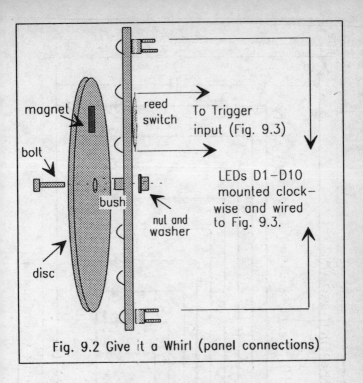

Fig. 9.2 Give it a Whirl (panel connections)

components. For wider viewing, a vertical version is preferable. The ten subjects suggested do not need to be used, and obviously the questions can be changed as soon as they have become familiar to contestants.

Typical Questions

TV:
1. What Australian 'soap' reminds you of football fixtures?
(Home and Away)
2. Who is the presenter of 'Blockbusters'?
(Bob Holness)
3. What TV detective series was set in Jersey?
(Bergerac)
4. Who was the Scotsman who pioneered Television?
(John Logie Baird)

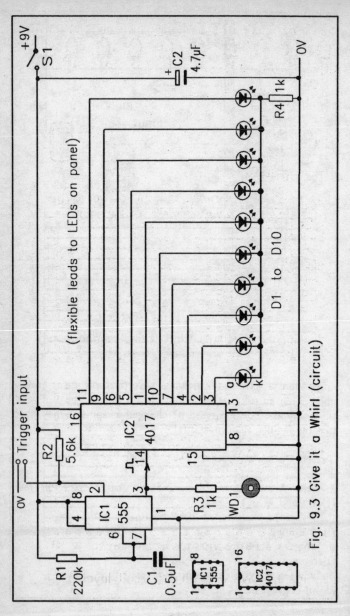

Fig. 9.3 Give it a Whirl (circuit)

54

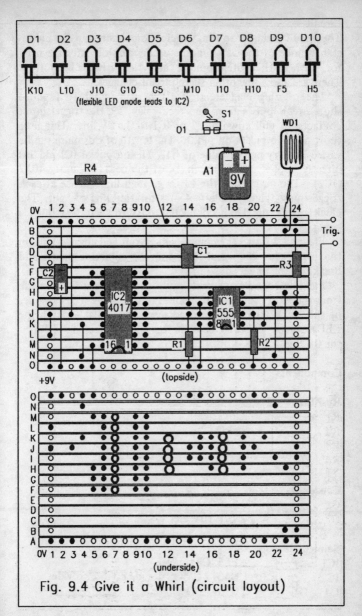

Fig. 9.4 Give it a Whirl (circuit layout)

Circuit

The circuit is similar to the Anticipation circuit, but the mono-stable mode of the 555 timer is used. This obviates the need for the 'TIME' potentiometer and the 'FREEZE' button. There are also a few other slight circuit changes.

The rotating magnet strobes the reed switch to produce short-circuit pulses from the reed relay, via the trigger input contacts, to pull down pin 2 of IC1 to the 0V line. This gives short positive pulses on pin 3. The length of this pulse can be varied by varying the value of C1. The output of IC1 pin 3 is directly applied to input pin 14 of the decade counter 4017 (IC2). The outputs to the LEDs go high in sequence at each trigger pulse, giving the effect of a rotating ring of light. The clock enable, pin 13, is connected to 0V to keep the sequence going.

Figure 9.4 shows the component layout and connections on the topside of the stripboard and the soldering points and breaks on the underside.

Flexible connections using multi-strand wire must be made from the IC2 outputs to the anodes of the LEDs. The cathodes of the LEDs (the short lead adjacent to the flat edge on the LED) can be all wired in common and connected via R4 to the 0V line.

Components

Resistors

R1	220kΩ
R2	5.6kΩ
R3	1kΩ
R4	1kΩ

Capacitors

C1	0.5μF
C2	4.7μF 10V elect.

Semiconductors

IC1	NE555CP timer
IC2	CD4017 CMOS decade counter/divider
D1 – D10	TIL20 LEDs

Loudspeakers
WD1   solid-state buzzer

Switches
S1   S.P.S.T. on/off

Miscellaneous
Plywood box, wheel, magnet, reed switch, stripboard, 9V
battery, wiring, etc.

Chapter 10

TIC-TAC-TOE

This is the American name for the old game of noughts and crosses. I prefer this name because, instead of pencilled noughts and crosses to indicate the state of play, we are using tri-colour LEDs that can indicate red, green and orange.

This simple game for two people can be played on scraps of old paper, in fact on any surface that will take pencil marks, as grown-ups have noticed. Why then, do we need an electronic version? Well, it's neat, attractive and easy to play especially when travelling. What's more, it has interesting possibilities for use in other games, which will be discussed later.

Construction
The front panel layout is shown in Figure 10.1. The nine tri-colour LEDs are mounted in the centre in the conventional noughts and crosses style. On either side, nine sockets are mounted and numbered 1 to 9 in similar formation. An on-off switch is centrally mounted. As with most electronic board games, because of the underside circuit components, a shallow compartment is needed below the board; for this project, a cigar box would serve admirably.

Game
The two contestants choose for red or green sides. The game proceeds exactly the same as noughts and crosses except that plugs are inserted alternately by each player in the socket replicas of the LED pattern; the red player plugs into the red sockets, the green player plugs into the green sockets. Each plug brings up the corresponding LED light in its relevant colour. Three reds or three greens in a vertical, horizontal or diagonal row wins the game. Be careful not to plug into a position that matches one already filled by your opponent because an orange-coloured LED loses you the game.

Variations
The third colour, orange, that occurs when both anodes of the

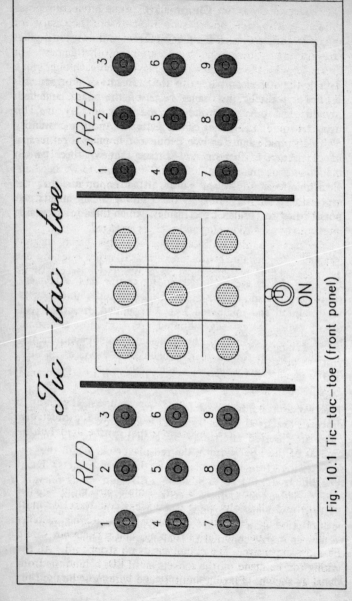

Fig. 10.1 Tic—tac—toe (front panel)

LED receive a positive voltage allows some interesting possibilities. Also, the on-off switch S1 is not necessary for noughts and crosses, because no current is drawn until plugs are inserted. However, it can be useful in other games. For instance, with the switch off, the players can each plug into a position and then switch on to see the location of opponent's LED (or possibly one orange LED) on the board, and then switch off for each to make the next move, and so on. This requires some memorising of the pattern. Another possibility is for the contestants to insert four or five plugs together in a blind attempt 'to have a row' (I mean a line of three!) when S1 is switched on.

With these additional games, it is important that the contestants do not see each other's plug arrangements. A small panel each side of the display can be fixed for screening purposes or extension plug and sockets arranged.

Quizzes are always interesting and this game suggests several. For instance, with the switch S1 off, a question can be asked of both contestants with alternative or yes or no answers. For example, a question might be:

What is the river that flows through Chester?

One, the River Trent?   Five, the River Dee? The contestants plug into either 1 or 5.

Switching S1 on now reveals the truth. If LED 5 is orange, both contestants know their geography; if LEDs 1 and 5 are red or green, then someone needs to revise. If LED1 is orange, both need to revise.

Obviously, a multi-answer question can be asked with up to nine answers that range from the sublime to the ridiculous.

These are only a few suggestions that can be used, but I'm sure you can think of more.

Circuit

The circuit, Figure 10.2, is very simple and requires little explanation. Possibly, some game ideas could ask for more than five plugs per player. Push-to-make latching switches would be a good alternative to plugs and sockets but would be more expensive. The circuit needs no stripboard. All the wiring can be made on the sockets and LEDs behind the front panel as shown. Flexible multi-strand wire must be used for

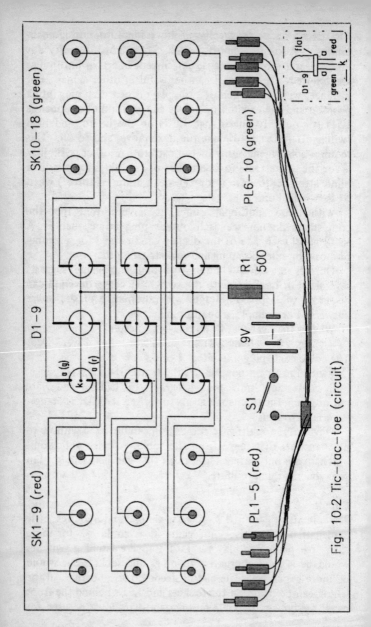

Fig. 10.2 Tic-tac-toe (circuit)

SK10–18 (green)

SK1–9 (red)

D1–9

PL6–10 (green)

PL1–5 (red)

R1 500

9V

S1

D1–9

flat
a
a
green red
k

62

the flying leads as these will be subject to considerable flexing.

Components

Resistors
R1   500Ω

Semiconductors
D1 – D9   LEDs (tri-colour)

Switches
S1   S.P.S.T.

Connectors
PL1 – 5   (2mm Marco C250 red)
PL6 – 10   (2mm Marco C252 green)
SK1 – 9   (2mm Marco C256 red 5.8mm fixing hole)
SK10 – 18   (2mm Marco C258 green 5.8mm fixing hole)

Miscellaneous
Plastic or plywood box, wiring, etc.

Chapter 11

SHOOTING STARS

This is a game that requires a good eye and a steady hand. It can be played by any number of contestants. As Figure 11.1 shows, the target board consists of two shooting stars against a

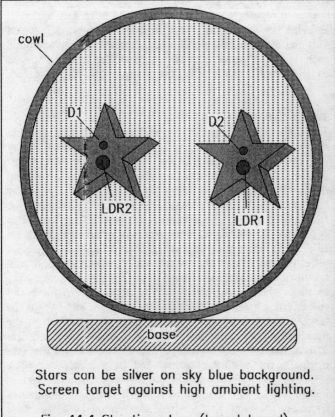

Stars can be silver on sky blue background.
Screen target against high ambient lighting.

Fig. 11.1 Shooting stars (target board)

sky blue background. Aim the trigger beam at the light-dependent resistor (LDR) in the centre of the left-hand star and the LED on the right-hand star should light. Now change your aim to the right-hand star, pull the trigger and hopefully the LED on the left-hand star will light. It sounds easy, and it would be if you were holding a torch and shining it from one LDR to the other. However, the trigger circuit is designed to give a single flash of short duration each time the trigger is pressed, no matter how long you keep your finger on the trigger. This means you must be on target when you press the trigger to register a hit, i.e. no possibility of an easy option of spraying the targets. If the light beam has too much spread you may need to separate the stars, or put a small tube around each LDR. A buzzer sounds each time you press the trigger, so the umpire can check how many shots you have had.

Trigger Circuit

The trigger circuit, Figure 11.2, makes use of the 555 timer in monostable mode. When pin 2 is connected to the 0V line by the TRIG pushbutton S2, pin 3 goes positive for a short duration determined by the time constant of capacitor C1 and the variable resistor VR1. This pulse time must be preset by trial and error to give a reasonable flash. The output pulse from pin 3 provides the base current via R3 to Tr1. This causes Tr1 to switch on momentarily and in turn switch on LP1. This needs to give a sharp beam of light so requires a reflector and lens. The switch and the lamp are best contained in a hand-held extension unit. Perhaps the easiest way to make this 'trigger beam' unit is to use an old torch and connect flexible leads to it, two to a switch and two to the lamp. Note that if the existing switch on a torch is of the pushbutton type and you want to use it, make sure you isolate it from the lamp. Otherwise, drill a hole in the end that was originally the battery container and fit a pushbutton (S2).

A typical stripboard layout for the trigger circuit is given in Figure 11.5. For ease of wiring, this has more strips than necessary. However, if desired, this circuit could be made smaller and incorporated in a hand-held trigger beam unit.

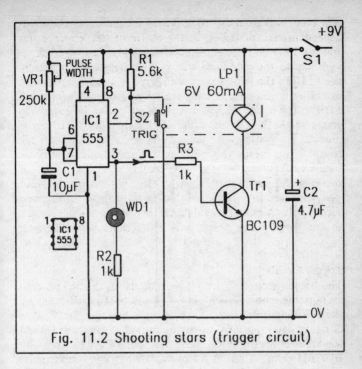

Fig. 11.2 Shooting stars (trigger circuit)

Target Circuit

The target circuit, Figure 11.3, is simply a two-transistor flip-flop. This type of circuit has two stable states and remains in one or the other unless switched over. The two collector loads are LEDs D1 and D2, each with a current-limiting resistor in series. Switch-over is achieved by light-dependent resistors in the base circuits. When the light beam is shone on LDR1, its resistance drops to a fraction of its 'dark-value'. This causes Tr1 to switch off, and the base current via cross-over resistor R2 flips on Tr2 and LED D2 lights. Conversely, the light beam shining on LDR2 lowers its resistance, switches off Tr2 (and D2), flips on Tr1 and causes LED D1 to light. For best results, the LDRs should be shielded against high ambient lighting.

The target layout, Figure 11.4, contains only six components so could easily be mounted behind the target board. If

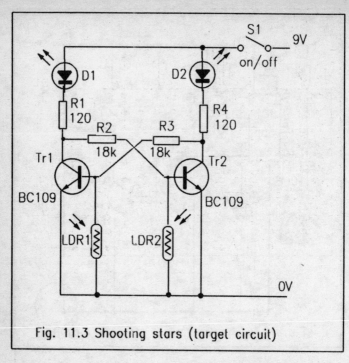

Fig. 11.3 Shooting stars (target circuit)

you prefer to experiment with a simpler layout than strip-board, then this circuit is a good candidate. It can be con-structed on the back of the target board by using only nine brass drawing pins, located roughly as shown in the target layout. All connections can be made on three pins for each transistor, two pins for the LED cathodes (k) and the remaining pin for the 9V line. If kitchen foil is used for the stars, make sure it does not short-circuit the leads of the LEDs or LDRs; use sleeving if necessary.

Variations

The trigger circuit, Figure 11.2, has other interesting applications. It can be used for a number of light beam games with LDRs. For instance, if an LDR used as a target in a game is coupled to the trigger input connections of the Trigger Counter (Figure 13.1) described in Chapter 13, then

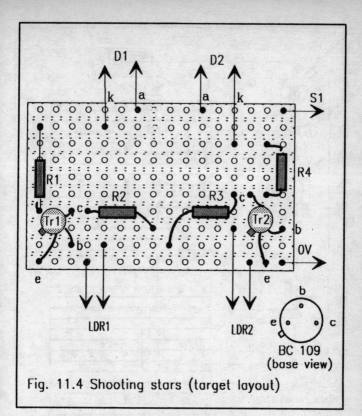

Fig. 11.4 Shooting stars (target layout)

the number of light-beam shots can be recorded on the counter to a maximum of ten. The game, which could be moving targets, clay pigeon shoots, etc., can then be reset for further play.

The LEDs D1 to D10 could be relocated into a straight line display or in whatever form the game suggests. With so many game variations using the Trigger Counter, it may be advisable to bring the IC2 outputs of Figure 13.1 out on to terminal strip.

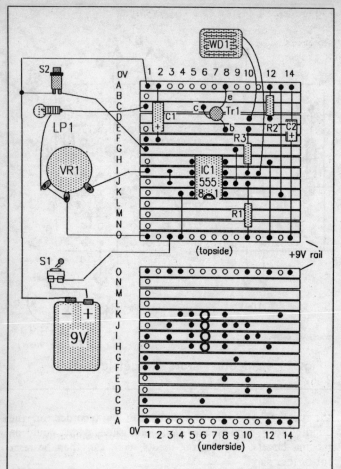

The layout of the components and connections shown on the topside of the stripboard. Notice the breaks to be made in the copper strip between the IC on the underside, and the soldering points.

Fig. 11.5 Shooting stars (trigger layout)

Components — Figure 11.2 Trigger Circuit

Resistors

R1	5.6kΩ
R2	1kΩ
R3	1kΩ

Potentiometers

VR1	250k potentiometer or preset

Capacitors

C1	10μF elect. 10V
C2	4.7μF elect. 10V

Semiconductors

IC1	NE555CP timer
Tr1	BC109

Switches

S1	S.P.S.T.
S2	pushbutton (non-locking)

Loudspeaker

WD1	solid-state buzzer

Lamps

LP1	6V 60mA

Miscellaneous

Lens and reflector, lampholder, 9V battery, stripboard, wiring, etc.

Components — Figure 11.3 Target Circuit

Resistors

R1	120Ω
R2	18kΩ
R3	18kΩ
R4	120Ω

Semiconductors

Tr1	BC109
Tr2	BC109
D1	LED
D2	LED
LDR1	light-dependent resistor ORP12
LDR2	light-dependent resistor ORP12

Switch

S1	S.P.S.T.

Miscellaneous

Target board and base, 9V battery, stripboard, wiring, etc.

Chapter 12

SHOVE-HA'PENNY

This is an up-to-date version of the game of shove-ha'penny, usually played by two persons or two sides, using five metal discs of old ha'penny size. Alternately, the opponents start by placing a disc overlapping the bottom edge of the board. This is struck by the ball of the thumb with sufficient weight to shove it up the board. All five discs are played from the bottom edge during a turn. A shallow box containing the electronic circuits, located under the bottom edge prevents the board from moving when a disc is shoved. The board is about 2 feet long by 15 inches wide. Ten one-and-quarter inch horizontal strips of metallised foil are affixed to the board with a narrow gap between each one. These may be glued separately, together with the base area towards the bottom starting edge. However, it is easier to glue the foil completely over the board and remove the ten $1/8''$ gaps, as shown in Figure 12.3, with a sharp knife. Note that the strips must be cut along the entire width of the foil so that they are isolated. The 0V and 'set' connections to the flip-flops can be a press fit under the left-hand batten that serves as the side of the board. This can be attached by two woodscrews.

Unlike the conventional game of shove-ha'penny, where the aim is to get the discs into one of these compartments or beds without the discs overlapping the gap between two adjacent strips, the game is more effective if you go for the lines. If two adjacent strips are short-circuited by a disc, one of five flip-flop circuits will be set depending on which strips are overlapped. This means that there is the possibility of bringing on up to five LEDs during a turn using five discs. Any LEDs that are lit during a turn would be credited to the player. The flip-flops would then be reset after the score is recorded. The player with the highest number of points after an agreed number of games, or who first attains an agreed number, say 25 or 50, is the winner.

Cannoning can be used to clear a disc off a bed and so switch on an LED. A disc that doesn't reach the first bed can

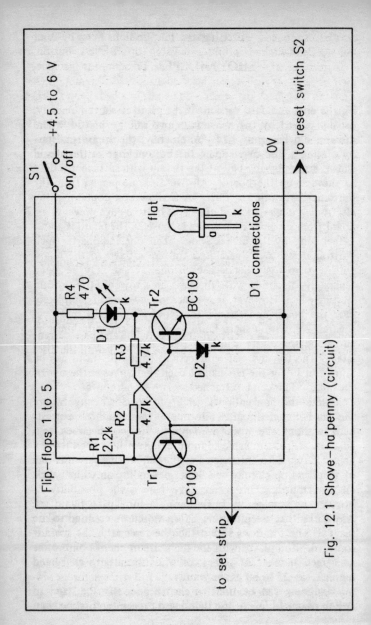

Fig. 12.1 Shove–ha'penny (circuit)

74

also be cannoned. After a turn, the flip-flops must be reset (all LEDs switched off) by pressing the RESET button.

A number of variations in play are possible, for instance, different colour LEDs can be used to give different points. You can also mark off when a disc lands in a bed, i.e. no LED lit, the winner being the first one to land in all the beds. A conventional game of shove-ha'penny can be played where the aim is to bring no LEDs on by going for the beds. However, discs not reaching the first bed would be retrieved and played again.

Circuit

The circuits used are simply five identical flip-flops, see Figure 12.1. When the switch S2 (RESET) is pressed, current flows via D2 and takes the base of Tr2 to 0V. This transistor switches off and turns the LED D1 off. Since S2 is common to all five flip-flops any LEDs coming on at switch-on will be switched off.

When a disc short-circuits two adjacent strips, the base of Tr1 is taken to the 0V line, and is switched off. Its collector voltage is derived via R1 from the supply line and base current flows via R2 for Tr2. This turns on the LED D1 until the discs are removed and the reset button is depressed.

Construction

The layout of the board is shown in Figure 12.3. It consists of a rectangular piece of plywood or hardboard about 15in by 24in. Test the metallised foil (baking foil) for conductivity before gluing it to the face of the board, making sure it is free of wrinkles. Cut away the 1/8" gaps as explained in Figure 12.2.

Affix battens to three sides, thick enough to retain the discs. Drill six holes in the right-hand batten to accommodate the five LEDs and RESET switch (see Figure 12.3), making sure that the foil strips don't short-circuit them. Insert the wire ends of the 'set' leads and 0V leads under the left-hand batten to make good contact with the foil strips before screwing this down. Make sure that the discs are flat and shiny to ensure that they make good electrical contact across the gaps

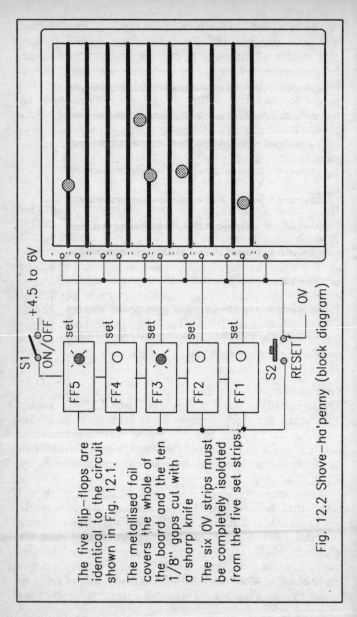

The five flip-flops are identical to the circuit shown in Fig. 12.1.

The metallised foil covers the whole of the board and the ten 1/8" gaps cut with a sharp knife

The six 0V strips must be completely isolated from the five set strips

Fig. 12.2 Shove-ha'penny (block diagram)

+4.5 to 6V

S1 ON/OFF

set FF5
set FF4
set FF3
set FF2
set FF1

S2 RESET

0V

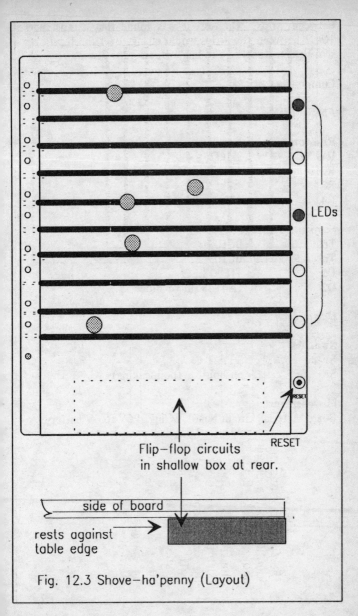

LEDs

Flip–flop circuits
in shallow box at rear.

RESET

side of board

rests against
table edge

Fig. 12.3 Shove–ha'penny (Layout)

between strips. On test, it was found that a resistance of 10kΩ between the strips would change over the flip-flop. If scoring is too easy, try rolling or tossing the discs.

Components

Five of each:

Resistors

R1	2.2kΩ
R2	4.7kΩ
R3	4.7kΩ
R4	470Ω

Semiconductors

Tr1	BC109
Tr2	BC109
D1	TIL20 LED
D2	1N4148 silicon diode

One of each:

Switches

S1	S.P.S.T.
S2	pushbutton (non-locking)

Miscellaneous
Board material, circuit board, wiring, 4.5V to 6V battery.

Chapter 13

GOING FOR GOLD

The getaway truck is standing by outside Fort Knox ready to load up the gold bullion. All you have to do is to remove the gold bars from the strong room one at a time and load them up without setting off too many alarms. An alarm is set off every time one of the bars touches both sides of the narrow passages that lead out from the strong room. The LEDs will light in numerical sequence as contact between sides is made. If the sides make contact nine times, the maximum alert LED will light and no more bars may be removed. Scoring can depend on the time taken to remove bars or the least number of alarm signals that sound and light up. The bars are moved by sliding them along the board with your finger. You may lift a bar over an LED 'sensor' that is not alight. However, if it is alight, you will have to find another way out. It is easy to vary the hazards even though, as you will realise, an alarm is only created by a short-circuit. For instance, one natural hazard could be a boundary fence.

Trigger Counter
This is the electronics side of the game, and a very useful accessory for a number of games in this book. It provides a ten LED display that can be triggered to count from the 'start' LED through to the tenth LED at each trigger input (a short-circuit). Here it remains until it is manually reset by a pushbutton. A short audible indication is given each time the counter steps on. Besides making this trigger counter circuit up for 'Going for Gold', as mentioned, it is applicable for other games in this book.

Remember that the trigger inputs can be given by:
— wires coming in contact; a sophisticated version of passing the ring around a metal loop can easily be constructed,
— make switches,
— reed switches,
— relay contacts,
— light-dependent resistors.

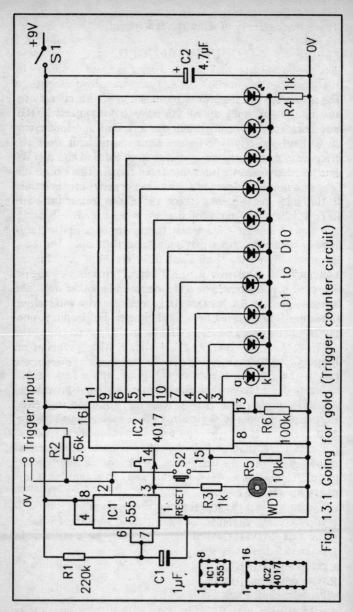

Fig. 13.1 Going for gold (Trigger counter circuit)

This provides plenty of scope for experiment.

Circuit
The circuit, Figure 13.1, of the trigger counter is similar to the Anticipation circuit, but there are some slight changes to watch out for. Instead of the astable mode, this circuit uses the monostable mode of the 555 timer, so no variable 'TIME' potentiometer is required and the 'FREEZE' pushbutton is no longer necessary. On receipt of a short-circuit from the trigger input contacts, pin 2 of IC1 is pulled down to the 0V line which produces a positive pulse of short duration on pin 3. This duration (less than a second) depends on the values of R1 and C1. Increase these values if a longer period is desired. The time constant is:

$$T = 0.64 \times CR \text{ (secs)}$$

where C is in farads and R is in ohms. This positive pulse on pin 3 is applied directly to the input, pin 14, of IC2, the decade counter. The LEDs light in sequence with each trigger pulse until D10 is reached. The output on pin 11 is now high and is tied to the clock enable, pin 13, which stops the sequence on D10. This LED (Maximum Alert), remains on until the RESET button is pressed to restart the sequence (D1 lit).

Figures 13.2 and 13.3 are the top and underside of the suggested game board layout. Figure 13.4 shows the strip-board layout for construction of the trigger counter circuit.

Components

Resistors

R1	220kΩ
R2	5.6kΩ
R3	1kΩ
R4	1kΩ
R5	10kΩ
R6	100kΩ

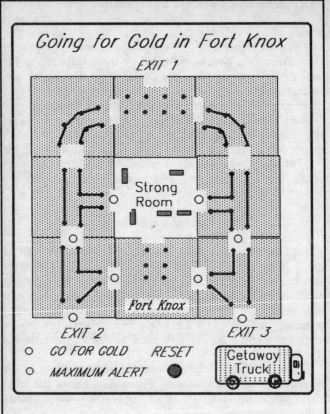

Going for Gold in Fort Knox

EXIT 1

Strong Room

Fort Knox

EXIT 2   EXIT 3

○ GO FOR GOLD   RESET

○ MAXIMUM ALERT   ●

Getaway Truck

The layout is made by copper pins with tinned copper wire links between the heads as shown. The LEDS are located at random except for the 'GO FOR GOLD' (D1) and the 'MAXIMUM ALERT' (D10).

Fig. 13.2 Going for gold (board layout)

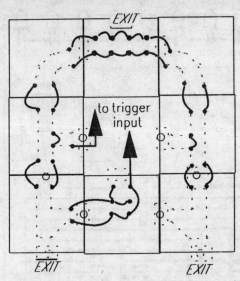

Fort Knox underground security plans

Solder the underside links on ends of copper pins protruding through board. When soldered, check there is no short–circuit between trigger input points.

Test by placing a gold bar across wires.

Fig. 13.3 Going for gold (underside layout)

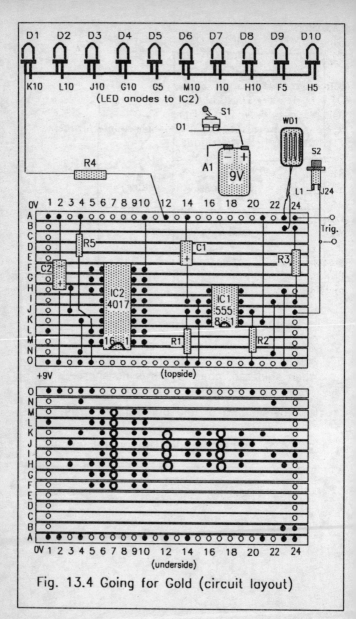

Fig. 13.4 Going for Gold (circuit layout)

Capacitors

| C1 | 1μF 10V elect. |
| C2 | 4.7μF 10V elect. |

Semiconductors

D1 – D10	TIL20 LEDs
IC1	NE555CP Timer
IC2	CD4017 CMOS decade counter/divider

Switches

| S1 | S.P.S.T. on/off |
| S2 | Pushbutton (non-locking) |

Loudspeakers

| WD1 | solid-state sounder |

Miscellaneous

Project box, plywood board, 9V battery, stripboard, wiring, metal bars, etc.

Chapter 14

TROLLEY TACTICS

Here's a Superstore race game where the trolley tactics can influence what you end up with at the checkouts. Trolleys can be very wayward; you push to the right and they move to the left and vice versa. However, in this game a wise trolley move can double the number of items you can take from a shelf.

The game can be played by up to four 'shoppers', who move in turn by the decade electronic dice around the store (see Figure 14.1). The speed of the counter can be adjusted so that a skilful shopper can anticipate the number that it 'freezes' on. The numbered LED will remain steady for a few seconds after the FREEZE button is pressed and this number dictates your move. You can move your trolley in any direction in one turn, but you are not allowed to go over the same square twice during the turn. For instance, if you get a 4 and want to be two squares ahead, you can go one sideways (left or right if not obstructed), two ahead, and one sideways (right or left).

If you reach a shelf that you have not already raided, you are permitted to take one item. You can then attempt to win an extra item by stopping the flashing bonus light on the shelf using the FREEZE button again. If you succeed, you take a bonus item off the shelf. However, if your shelf LED does not light, another of the nine LEDs will remain steady for a few seconds. During this period, a shopper, or shoppers, adjacent to another LED that lights can help themselves to an extra item provided they do not already have two. After a shelf has been raided of one item (or possibly two if the light was on) the shopper proceeds to the next counter to collect the next item, and so on. Shoppers cannot use the bonus button again once they have got one item off a particular shelf, but may benefit from another shopper's miscalculation if adjacent to a bonus light. The game ends when a shopper has collected an item (or two) from each shelf or after an agreed time. The value of the items in each trolley is then

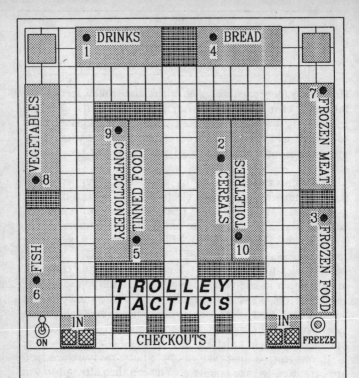

Fig. 14.1 Trolley tactics (front panel)

totted up at the checkouts, the one with the highest value being the winner. It's the lolly in your trolley that counts!

Circuit

The circuit, Figure 14.2, is the familiar astable 555 timer followed by the 4017 decade counter, as described in the Anticipation circuit of Chapter 1. The slight differences are that no dice facility is given and an electrolytic capacitor C3 is connected to pin 13 of the 4017. This capacitor charges up when the FREEZE button is pushed and discharges

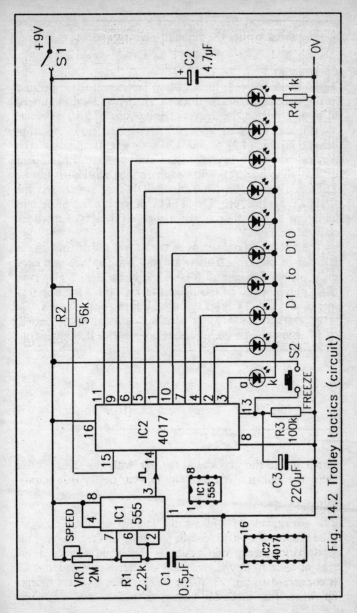

Fig. 14.2 Trolley tactics (circuit)

89

gradually through R3. The effect is to hold the LED on for about 7 seconds after the pushbutton is released.

Construction

Again, the board calls for a shallow box construction because of the electronics 'below ground' The ten LEDs do not need to be laid out on the shelves in any particular kind of order. Multi-strand insulated leads should be used from the stripboard (Figure 14.3) to the LEDs to give flexibility. The playing board can be made from stiff cardboard, hardboard or thin plywood. You will need to drill ten small holes for the LEDs and two larger holes for the ON/OFF switch and the FREEZE pushbutton. The SPEED control can also be mounted in one of the other corners if in-games changes of speed are thought desirable.

The number of item cards on the shelves will depend on the number of players. If there are four players, then you need eight per shelf in case all players win bonus items. However, these only need to be small pieces of card with a value on (say 50p or £1.50). The backs of the cards can either have a cold statement such as 'Fish' or be more imaginatively decorated.

Different colour shapes can be designed for the trolleys out of plastic.

Components

Resistors

R1	2.2kΩ
R2	56kΩ
R3	100kΩ
R4	1kΩ

Potentiometers

| VR1 | 2MΩ (linear) |

Capacitors

C1	0.5µF
C2	4.7µF 10V
C3	220µF 10V

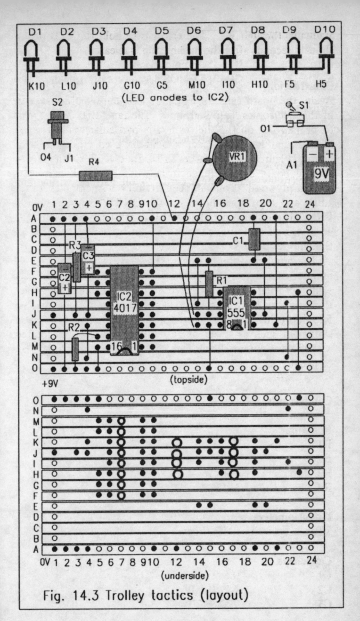

Fig. 14.3 Trolley tactics (layout)

Semiconductors

D1 – D10	TIL20 LEDs
IC1	NE555CP timer IC
IC2	CD4017 CMOS decade counter/divider

Switches

S1	S.P.S.T.
S2	pushbutton (non-locking)

Miscellaneous

Board, trolley shapes, item cards, 9-volt battery, wiring, etc.

Chapter 15

PIT-STOP

Pit-stop is a motor-racing game for up to four competitors, the winner being the first driver past the chequered flag after a pre-arranged number of laps. A driver can move away from the starting grid only when he has 'tanked up'. Fuelling and moves (distance round the track) are determined by an electronic indicator, the number of moves depending on skill in selecting the numbered LEDs that flash in sequence. Each move results in fuel being used up and the state of each fuel tank is monitored by a fuel gauge. Lack of fuel is shown by the 'EMPTY TANK' indicator light; drivers must then stop to 'TANK SELECT' and refuel before any further movement. In addition to the 'drive' and 'refuel' operations, there are hazards and advantages along the track dictated by cards.

Pit-stops can be enforced by card selection and, in a more realistic version of the game where refuelling is confined to the pits, also made at a driver's discretion. If this rule applies, a 'TANK EMPTY' light on when the car is out on the track puts the driver out of the race.

Circuit

The circuit diagram can be considered as four basic blocks:
- the clock generator, which provides the timing pulses for controlling the decader counter;
- the decade counter and ten-LED flashing display that can be stopped momentarily to indicate either 'refuel' or 'drive distance' outputs, selectable by the players;
- four tank capacitors, chargeable when tank-up switches are pressed;
- the comparator, controlling the 'tank empty' light, and a meter that monitors fuel levels.

In Figure 15.1, the clock generator, IC1, is the popular CMOS 555 timer used in the astable multivibrator mode. The frequency of oscillation is controlled by the fixed capacitor C1, and the variable resistor VR1 (SPEED). Output pulses are available on pin 3.

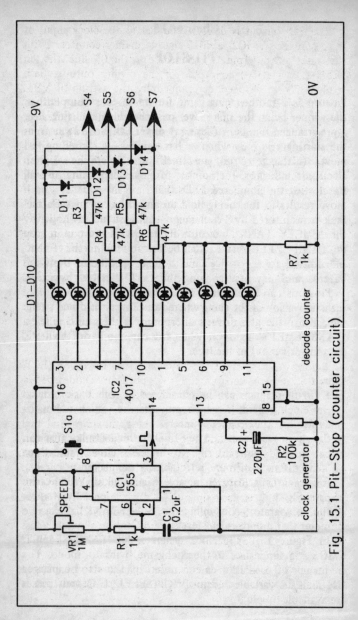

Fig. 15.1 Pit–Stop (counter circuit)

The 555 output is directly coupled to the clock input of integrated circuit IC2, a 4017 decade divider/counter. With the 'reset' output (pin 15) connected to the 0V line, the ten LEDs (D1 − D10) connected in the divider outputs flash sequentially at a speed determined by the setting of VR1. Normally, VR1 is set so that the counter output LEDs flash at several times per second. During a turn, when S1 is pressed, contact S1a 'freezes' the display on one LED for a few seconds before flashing resumes. The rate of flashing should be fast enough so that some skill is required to anticipate the selection of a particular LED. However, for younger players, it may help to select a slower speed with VR1.

As shown in Figure 15.2, each player has a tank (electrolytic capacitors C3 − C6) that can be charged via a 'TANK-UP' switch (S4 − S7). Four of the outputs of the counter are coupled via resistors (R3 − R6 on Figure 15.1) to the 'TANK-UP' switches. During refuelling, when a selected output is 'frozen' for a few seconds, if the relevant 'TANK-UP' switch is pressed, the positive voltage on the output pin is connected via the 47kΩ resistor and switched to charge the driver's tank capacitor. If by misjudgement another driver's LED is selected, then the other driver can press his or her 'TANK-UP' button and take-on some fuel.

Before pressing the 'GO' switch S1, the 'TANK SELECT' switch S2 must be set to the player's position. Diodes D15 − D18 isolate the tank capacitors and prevent any short-circuiting of charges if the rotary contacts of S2 should make-before-break. Switch S2 connects the comparator and fuel meter to monitor the state of the player's fuel tank capacitor. It also connects the tank capacitor to a discharge circuit, when S1 is pressed, formed by R10 and C8 connected in parallel. On each turn, a player's tank is discharged slightly by this circuit, i.e. fuel is used up on the drive, especially if short distances are selected. Switch S3, 'DRAIN TANK', serves two purposes: it can be used with a 'Hazard Card' to simulate a loss of fuel situation, or (at all positions of the 'TANK SELECT' switch) to drain tanks for the next game.

Diodes D11 to D14 enable tank capacitors to be charged via the 'TANK-UP' pushbuttons if the 'ALL' refuel light is 'on'.

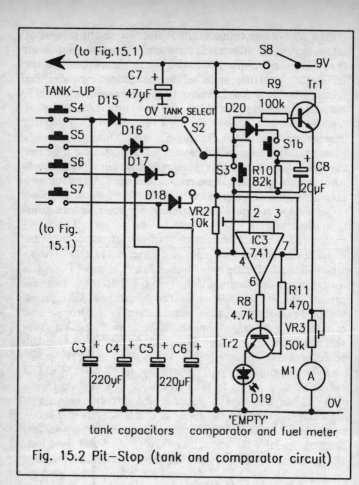

Fig. 15.2 Pit-Stop (tank and comparator circuit)

The comparator is a 741 operational amplifier, IC3, which monitors the voltage in a tank capacitor and compares it with a reference voltage set by potentiometer VR2. When the voltage level in the connected tank capacitor falls below the reference voltage, output pin 6 of the comparator goes high; this switches on transistor Tr2 and the 'TANK EMPTY' LED lights. A 'TANK-UP' operation is then required.

Switch S2 also connects the fuel meter circuit to a driver's tank circuit for monitoring purposes. Transistor Tr1 is connected as an emitter-follower, the high input impedance preventing excessive drain on the tank capacitor. The 'fuel' reading on the micro-ammeter in the emitter circuit is set by the series preset resistor VR3.

Construction

The prototype was constructed on a 15in square 3-ply board, layout as shown in Figure 15.3, with four 2in × ¼in strips for the sides. The clock generator and decade counter were mounted on a separate piece of 0.1in stripboard as this circuit is a useful electronic-dice equivalent for several board games.

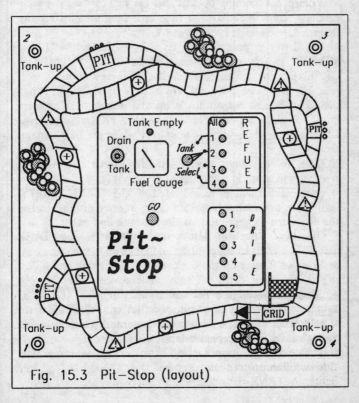

Fig. 15.3 Pit–Stop (layout)

The track layout can be an enlarged replica of the one shown, or can be modified to incorporate other ideas, especially if the constructor is a motor-racing enthusiast.

Playing

1. Before starting, switch on and make sure that the four tanks are discharged by pressing the 'DRAIN TANK' switch while rotating the 'TANK SELECT' switch.

2. Set the 'SPEED' switch to an agreed speed.

3. Select 'GO' in turn to decide order of play, by highest drive positions, and which two cars will be in pole (front) positions.

NOTE: Only two cars can be abreast at any time during a race, so a third car 'coming up fast' behind two cars on the same patch of track will have to tuck in behind and forfeit any extra distance selected for the move.

4. The driver in pole position starts by switching the 'TANK SELECT' switch to his position (RED, BLUE, YELLOW or GREEN). For instance, when the RED switch position is selected as shown, the red driver tries to anticipate when the LED for the red output is on and presses 'GO' momentarily to select it. If successful, he then presses his 'TANK-UP' switch to charge up his tank only while the LED remains on.

NOTE: Holding down the 'TANK-UP' switch after flashing resumes will result in some loss of fuel.

Successful fuelling is indicated if the 'TANK EMPTY' lamp goes off, and a driver can select a 'drive distance' when the next turn comes round, or elect to tank-up further.

5. The next driver in pole position, switches the 'TANK SELECT' switch to his position and tanks-up in the same way.

6. The two drivers on the back row of the starting grid follow suit, but cannot drive off until at least one driver in pole-position has moved (the 'no-passing two' rule).

7. At the beginning of a turn, on 'TANK SELECT', if the 'TANK EMPTY' light is on, a driver must tank-up. Any 'Drive' moves selected inadvertently are forfeited.

8. If the ALL position is selected, all drivers can press their 'TANK-UP' button to take on fuel.

Hazard Cards (!)

* Oil spill – miss a turn
* Spin off track – miss a turn
* Slow-down for chicane – reduce drive by 1
* Tank holed – press 'DRAIN TANK'
* Aqua-planing – compulsory '1' pit-stop to fit 'wet' tyres
* Engine overheating – compulsory pit-stop one turn
* Puncture – reduce drives by one and compulsory '1' pit-stop.

Advantage Cards (+)

* Super-fuel! – add 2 to drive score
* Engine finely tuned-up – add 1 to drive score
* Following wind – double drive score
* Reserve tank – perform 'Tank-up'
* Double accelerate – hold card until needed
* Close gap – tuck in behind car immediately in front
* Good road-holding – hold card and add 1 to drive score on next bend.

Components

Resistors

R1	1kΩ
R2	100kΩ
R3	47kΩ
R4	47kΩ
R5	47kΩ
R6	47kΩ
R7	1kΩ
R8	4.7kΩ
R9	100kΩ
R10	82kΩ
R11	470Ω

Potentiometers

VR1	1MΩ potentiometer
VR2	10kΩ preset
VR3	50kΩ preset

Capacitors

C1	0.2μF
C2	220μF elect. 10V
C3 – C6	220μF elect. 10V
C7	47μF elect. 10V
C8	20μF elect. 10V

Semiconductors

IC1	NE555CP timer
IC2	CD4017 CMOS decade counter/divider
IC3	741 op-amp comparator
Tr1	BC109
Tr2	BC109
D1	TIL20 LED (ALL REFUEL)
D2 – D5	TIL20 LEDs (REFUEL)
D6 – D10	TIL20 LEDs (DRIVE)
D11 – D18	1N4148 silicon diodes
D19	TIL20 LED (EMPTY)
D20	1N4148 silicon diode

Switches

S1	2-pole pushbutton non-locking
S2	single-pole, 4-way rotary
S3	pushbutton (non-locking)
S4 – S7	pushbutton (non-locking)
S8	S.P.S.T.

Meters

M1	Micro-ammeter

Chapter 16

WHERE IN THE WORLD!

Only recently on the radio it was stated that a survey showed that many teenagers didn't even know where Great Britain was on a map of the world. It didn't state where in the world the survey was taken!

This triggered off an idea for a simple board game that will quickly remedy the situation, when the quizmaster asks, 'Where in the world is . . . ?' In this game, the contestant's response to this is to try to place a detector unit on the spot of the country asked for on the map of the world, see Figure 16.1. This blank map can be reproduced at a suitable size on a photocopier, or a map traced from an atlas, and pasted on hardboard or plywood. If the country is correctly located, the LED on the detector will light. The contestant scores a point and the quizmaster can then continue with a different country for the same or another contestant.

The detector is similar to that used in Figure 3.5 in the Buried Treasure game. It simply uses an LED in series with a limiting resistor, reed switch and 9V battery. However, an extra pushbutton can be added in series, which has to be pressed when the detector is assumed to be in the right position. This prevents the player sweeping the detector around to find the correct spot. The reed switch is actuated by a magnet at the rear of the selected country. Some thought went into working out how the magnet could quickly be transferred from one country to another by the quizmaster. Tape or Plasticine seemed to be a little too primitive. However, this sticky problem became screamingly obvious. A magnet attracts, and if it attracts a drawing pin then the attraction is mutual. Drawing pins were pressed into the rear of the map adjacent to the name of the country (see Figure 16.2). The magnet is readily attracted to a pin, and could easily be transferred from one spot to another after a successful search. A few of the major countries have been indicated on the rear of the map. Each country listed on the rear, is indicated by an unnamed spot on the map directly in front of

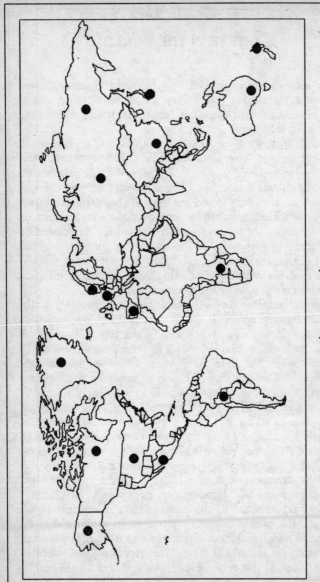

Fig. 16.1 Where in the world! (front view)

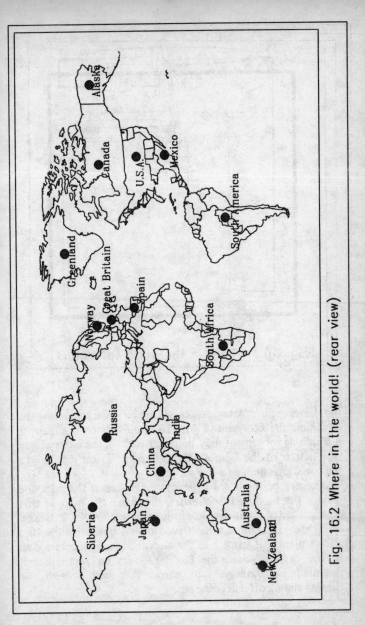

Fig. 16.2 Where in the world! (rear view)

103

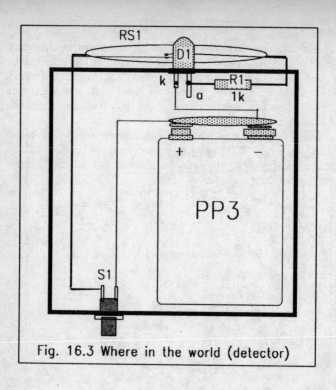

Fig. 16.3 Where in the world (detector)

the drawing pin. Attempts may either be made by placing the electronic detector unit (Figure 16.3) directly on the map, or a searching movement may be permitted. In the latter case, a stop watch or the Games Timer (Chapter 7) can be used to impose a time limit of a few seconds.

The size of the board depends on the size of the map, the greater the number of countries, the larger the map so that adjacent small countries don't all come within the magnetic influence of the same magnet position. A board 14in × 10in allows plenty of space. As the electronic components are all in the detector unit, the board requires no depth, but if mounted horizontally, four corner feet will prevent the magnet sliding off a drawing pin.

Variations

As usual, there are some interesting variations in this game idea; you have probably thought of them. The map can be your local one, say a map of Australia, England, Ireland, Scotland, Wales, New Zealand or the U.S.A. and indicating counties, states or major cities. All you need to change the location is a map outline.

This idea can also be used with a sheet of general knowledge answers. The questions are held and asked by the quizmaster, having placed the magnet behind the correct square on the answer sheet.

Components

Resistors
R1   1kΩ

Semiconductors
D1   TIL20 LED

Switches
S1   pushbutton (non-locking)
RS1   reed switch

Miscellaneous
Detector box, map board, 9V battery PP3

Chapter 17

SPIN THE WHEEL

Spinning a wheel is always fun, especially when waiting for it to slow up, or is it down! Here is a simple circuit, Figure 17.1, that gives a flashing light, alternately red and green, as the wheel turns and slows up to stop on one or the other of the colours. This project is most suitable for the constructor who is more mechanically, than electronically minded. Circuit-wise it is very simple. The wheel is divided into about twenty segments, numbered or labelled in whatever manner you desire. The flashing light is provided by a tri-colour LED mounted behind, or above, the wheel, and indicates which section to choose when it stops flashing. The red or green indication can be used for some other purpose in a game; double the score on green for instance, have another go, or red to stop and green to proceed, etc.

The alternate flashing is produced by the movement of a lever over studs, distributed evenly around the periphery of the wheel, when the wheel is rotated. In turn, this lever, depending on whether it is actuated or not, switches over a changeover micro-switch which applies the positive voltage alternately to the red and green anodes of the tri-colour LED. If make-before-break change-over contacts of a key-switch were used in place of the micro-switch, then the orange colour of the LED would be produced between the red and green.

Some experiment will be necessary to get the movement of the lever and micro-switch operating correctly. The lever should be flexible to allow for any inaccuracy when lining up the studs. A spring-steel strip will be suitable. The length will depend on the diameter of the wheel and the distance between the studs. Preferably, a plastic translucent wheel should be used so that the LED can be mounted behind. In this case, for the studs you can use small nuts and bolts. If a hardboard or plywood wheel is used, the LED will have to be mounted above it where it can be seen. For economy, copper nails, available in most DIY stores, can be used in place

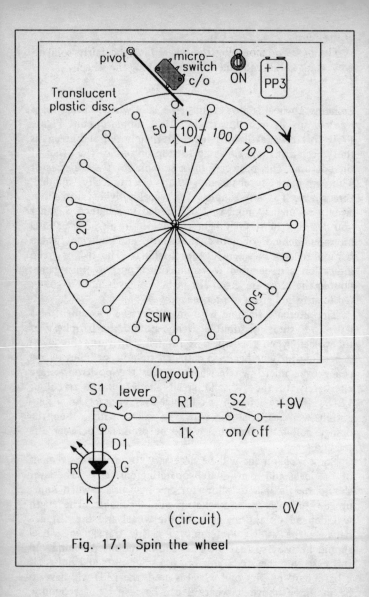

Fig. 17.1 Spin the wheel

108

of the studs.

The base for mounting the wheel must be fairly solid to prevent any other movement when spinning the wheel.

Components

Resistors

R1   1kΩ

Switches

S1   Micro-switch (change-over)
S2   S.P.S.T.

Semiconductor

D1   tri-colour LED

Miscellaneous

Wheel, studs and base, 9V battery, wiring, etc.

Chapter 18

CALLING THE TUNE

This is a game for two players or two teams. The aim is to choose the first ten notes of a well-known tune. The game uses a slow-running decade counter (see Chapter 1) to determine which note, previously set up in a sequence of ten pushbuttons, to select.

Use the decade counter to determine who goes first by taking turns to select the highest number. The game is on! The first counter number selected determines which of the ten pushbuttons must be pressed to sound a note of the tune. To guess a tune by sounding one note is pretty futile, but to make things easier, this note will be sounded together with the tapped rhythm of the other nine notes not yet selected. This musical combination must be sounded by the person who has set up the tune, preferably a musician. It is most unlikely that the contestant in play will recognise the tune at this stage, but the opportunity is given to 'call the tune'. If the tune is not identified, the next player operates the counter to choose another note, and so on. When sufficient notes are sounded progressively, the player to 'call the tune' correctly is the winner. Selected notes are chalked up as shown in Figure 18.1 to remind the 'musician' which pushbuttons to press. The counter speed is adjusted to be slow enough for a skilful player to select the note he requires to recognise the tune. If a note chosen has already been selected, the turn is forfeited and the next contestant has a turn. If teams are playing, then it is fairer for the players in each side to have alternate turns.

Construction
The components for the basic circuit are few and can be mounted on a small piece of stripboard. Figure 18.1 shows the underside with the solder points and the four breaks in the copper strip under the 555 integrated circuit. The components shown are on the other side of the stripboard and have been angled towards their respective solder points in the interests of clarity.

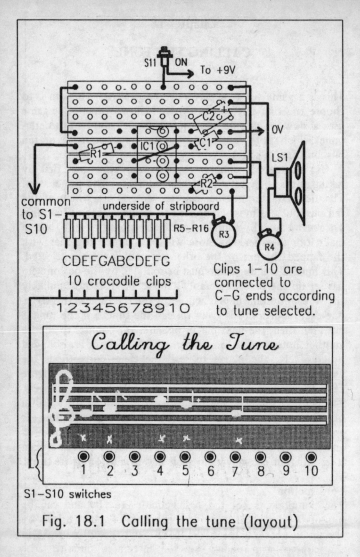

Fig. 18.1 Calling the tune (layout)

The board can be made of 3-ply, the size being dependent on the size of the row of ten pushbuttons. A convenient size for social activities is about 9in by 18in (229mm by 458mm;

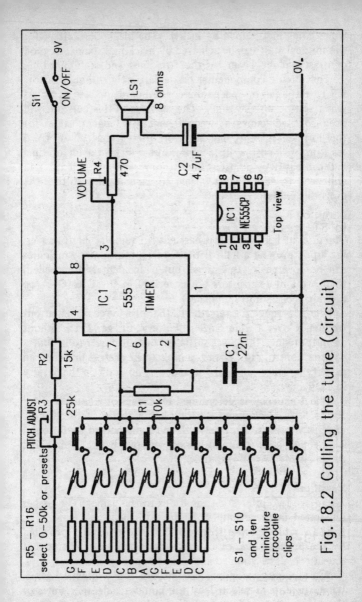

Fig.18.2 Calling the tune (circuit)

113

we're going metric inch by inch!). The blackboard effect for the musical staff can be achieved by black matt paint. A good contrast will be given by the five lines and staff in white.

The circuit components, particularly, the tuning resistors R5 to R16, can be spaced under the board for ease of access when setting up the tune. The resistors in this network will need selected values between 0 and 50k, higher values for the lower notes. Using skeleton presets instead of fixed resistors will cost a little more, but will save a lot of time and can easily be adjusted against a musical instrument. You will need to add a short busbar to each resistor to take the crocodile clip(s).

Circuit

The circuit, Figure 18.2, is basically an audio generator covering an octave and a half of the C major scale. Many melodies can be covered by this range, but if accidentals are needed, then eight more resistors are necessary in the C to G′ range provided (black notes on piano).

The 555 timer is a versatile IC that provides a stable output frequency over a wide range of battery voltage. Even without an output stage there was sufficient output power to include a volume control R4. If the game is to be played in a hall, an amplifying stage can easily be added. The drain on the battery is small.

The frequency is determined by capacitor C1, the resistor R5 to R16 selected and R3 the pitch adjuster. Capacitor C1 charges via this resistor network and is discharged via R1 only. As a rough guide to tuning values, with 60k between pin 7 and the positive rail a 'B' is sounded.

Variations

There are two interesting variations to the game. The first is illustrated in the example of Happy Birthday in Figure 18.3. If the opening phrase is longer than the ten notes provided by the pushbuttons, or to make the game easier, notes that repeat can all be sounded and chalked up in one turn.

The second variation also makes for a quicker game. Whatever note is selected by the counter, all other notes of the same pitch can be sounded and chalked up. For instance,

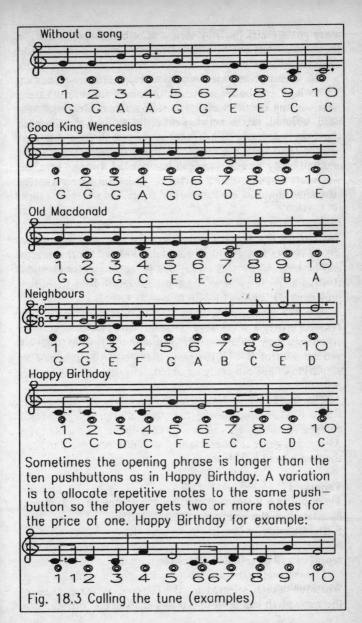

Without a song

1	2	3	4	5	6	7	8	9	10
G	G	A	A	G	G	E	E	C	C

Good King Wenceslas

1	2	3	4	5	6	7	8	9	10
G	G	G	A	G	G	D	E	D	E

Old Macdonald

1	2	3	4	5	6	7	8	9	10
G	G	G	C	E	E	C	B	B	A

Neighbours

1	2	3	4	5	6	7	8	9	10
G	G	E	F	G	A	B	C	E	D

Happy Birthday

1	2	3	4	5	6	7	8	9	10
C	C	D	C	F	E	C	C	D	C

Sometimes the opening phrase is longer than the ten pushbuttons as in Happy Birthday. A variation is to allocate repetitive notes to the same push-button so the player gets two or more notes for the price of one. Happy Birthday for example:

1	1	2	3	4	5	6	6	7	8	9	10

Fig. 18.3 Calling the tune (examples)

115

in Neighbours, if pushbutton 2 is selected by the counter, 'G' is sounded, but pushbutton 5 may be sounded because this is also a 'G'.

As only one note is sounded at a time, one oscillator can provide all ten notes. The front of the board has the treble clef and the five lines of the musical staff on which the notes are chalked when selected. Below the staff are the ten push-buttons, numbered 1 — 10 that sound out the first ten notes of the tune. All the numbered pushbuttons selected by the present and previous turns can be operated during a turn, and these are marked off by a cross for convenience. As stated, these pushbuttons are pressed and the rest of the notes tapped in rhythm.

Previously, each tune must be set up on the rear of the board by a non-player before play. This involves clipping ten flying leads on to R5 to R16, suitably lettered for the selected tune. Plugs and sockets may be used instead of the crocodile clips if these are available. Some tunes will have more than one note on the same pitch, so several sockets are needed for each note C to G.

A number of tunes are given, but many more can be work-ed out by yourself or a musical friend. Remember that the rhythm must also be tapped out on (and off) the pushbuttons by someone musical.

Components

Resistors

R1	10kΩ
R2	15kΩ
R3	25kΩ preset
R4	470Ω preset
R5 — R16	select on test (or 50kΩ presets)

Capacitors

C1	22nF
C2	4.7µF 10V elect.

Semiconductors

IC1	NE555CP Timer

Loudspeaker
LS1   8Ω

Switches
S1 – S10   pushbutton (non-locking)
S11   S.P.S.T.

Miscellaneous
Plywood board, stripboard, 9V battery, miniature crocodile clips (10 off)

Chapter 19

DEMANDE ET REPONSE

This is obviously a question and answer game. A rotary switch allows eight questions to be selected and an array of twelve pushbuttons offer possible answers, some multi-choice. The correct answer is acknowledged by a light-emitting diode. Overlays of different subjects can be used to answer, and a simple encoder for up to eight sheets prevents the answer positions being easily memorised. To enable multiple answers to some of the eight questions, four extra pushbuttons are used in AND-gate arrangements.

Circuit
The block diagram Figure 19.1 shows a very simple series circuit where the '1' rotary switch position has been selected. Basically, the circuit consists of a 3-volt battery in series with an LED and a switching arrangement. A 9V PP3 battery can be used in which case a 1k limiting resistor must be inserted in series. The full circuit diagram is shown in Figure 19.2.

Switching Arrangement
A single-pole, 8-way switch, S13, determines which question is asked. The eight positions are each wired to one separate pin of the octal socket SK1. The octal plug PL1 should have no locking spigot; file it off if one is present so that the plug can be rotated through the eight positions. The eight wires from the plug must be multi-flex to allow free movement. These wires connect to the eight pushbuttons as shown. You will notice that some pushbuttons are series connected to allow for the multi-choice questions. These are effectively 2-input AND gates. The prototype model had a 12-way question switch and some 3-input AND gates, but this arrangement is sufficient to show the basic idea. The common lead from the pushbuttons is connected to the anode of the LED.

The octal plug and socket encoding arrangement is secretly organised by the quizmaster according to the selected quiz

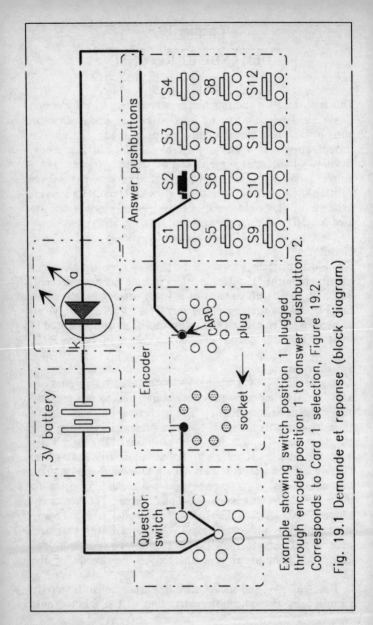

Example showing switch position 1 plugged through encoder position 1 to answer pushbutton 2. Corresponds to Card 1 selection, Figure 19.2.

Fig. 19.1 Demande et reponse (block diagram)

120

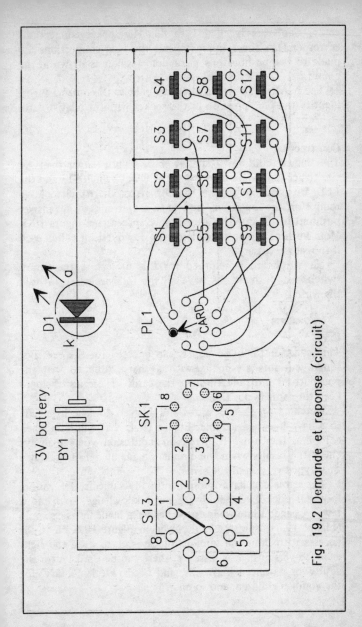

Fig. 19.2 Demande et reponse (circuit)

121

card. Cards are labelled 1 to 8. The socket connections correspond to these numbers, but the plug connections are made to the pushbuttons in random fashion as shown in the circuit.

The 'CARD' arrow on the plug enables the quizmaster to identify the plug position in the socket with the relative card.

Construction

The unit is built on a shallow box slightly larger than A4 size to accommodate the cards. The 8-way switch S13 and the LED are mounted in the top corners of the panel to leave room for the questions and answer buttons. The answer pushbuttons S1 to S12 are suitably spaced; see Figure 19.3. More buttons can be added and a 12-way question switch used if thought necessary.

No stripboard is required for this project as the rotary switch and pushbuttons have all the tags necessary to hold the wiring.

Cards

Thin card, or thick A4 paper, can be used for the overlays; square cut-outs are made with a sharp knife so that the pushbuttons protrude through the card. These also help to keep the cards in position.

Matching up the questions and answers took a little time so I have included a table, Figure 19.4, that will help when compiling the cards. If there is any confusion, you can always check the results when the circuit is made up before making a final typed version of the cards.

The cards can have questions on any subjects, TV, music, football, cricket, geography, general knowledge, to name a few. A general knowledge card has been made up as a sample (Figure 19.5) using the table given in Figure 19.4. It is not necessary to limit the number of cards, 1 to 8, to the eight encoded versions. For instance, there can be Card 1A for the adults, or advanced know-alls, and Card 1E (elementary) for the younger children, and so on.

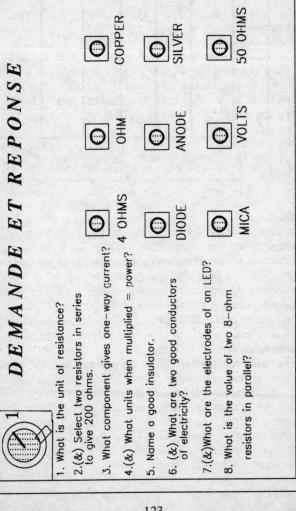

DEMANDE ET REPONSE

1. What is the unit of resistance?
2. (&) Select two resistors in series to give 200 ohms.
3. What component gives one-way current?
4. (&) What units when multiplied = power?
5. Name a good insulator.
6. (&) What are two good conductors of electricity?
7. (&) What are the electrodes of an LED?
8. What is the value of two 8-ohm resistors in parallel?

4 OHMS   OHM   COPPER   CATHODE

DIODE   ANODE   SILVER   150 OHMS

MICA   VOLTS   50 OHMS   AMPS

CARD 1A

Fig. 19.3 Demande et reponse (layout)

123

1	2	3	4	5	6	7	8
Answer pushbuttons for 1–8 plug rotation							
2	11+8	5	10+12	9	3+7	6+4	1
11+8	5	10+12	9	3+7	6+4	1	2
5	10+12	9	3+7	6+4	1	2	11+8
10+12	9	3+7	6+4	1	2	11+8	5
9	3+7	6+4	1	2	11+8	5	10+12
3+7	6+4	1	2	11+8	5	10+12	9
6+4	1	2	11+8	5	10+12	9	3+7
1	2	11+8	5	10+12	9	3+7	6+4

Fig. 19.4 Demande et reponse (encoding table)

Components

Switches
S1 – S12   pushbuttons (non-locking)
S13   rotary, 8-way, single-pole

Semiconductors
D1   TIL20 LED

Miscellaneous
Box, plywood or plastic, 12in × 9in approx., battery, wiring.

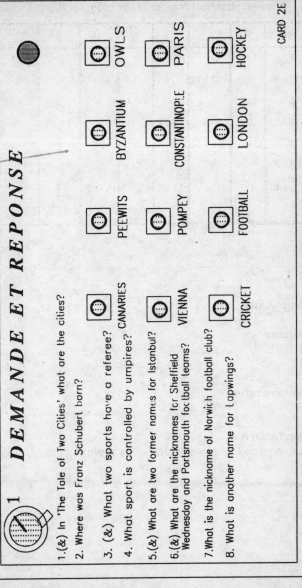

DEMANDE ET REPONSE

1.(&) In 'The Tale of Two Cities', what are the cities?

2. Where was Franz Schubert born?

3. (&) What two sports have a referee?

4. What sport is controlled by umpires?

5.(&) What are two former names for Istanbul?

6.(&) What are the nicknames for Sheffield Wednesday and Portsmouth football teams?

7.What is the nickname of Norwich football club?

8. What is another name for Lapwings?

CANARIES   PEEWITS   BYZANTIUM   OWLS

VIENNA   POMPEY   CONSTANTINOPLE   PARIS

CRICKET   FOOTBALL   LONDON   HOCKEY

CARD 2E

Fig. 19.5 Demande et reponse (Sample Card 2 layout)

125

Chapter 20

ELECTRONIC SKITTLES

These are skittles that you won't need to stand up after scoring a hit. Swing a magnet on the end of a cord to register a hit and the skittle will light up. Count up the number of hits after three swings, then simply press a button to reset for the next contestant. The magnet must be adjusted to be very close to the top of the centre skittle. If your magnet is not too strong then the alternative skittle where the reed switch is affixed along the top may be more reliable. Test the distance needed to actuate the reed switch before deciding. The longer the cord, the more constant the distance between magnet and reed switch. An 80cm cord gives less than a centimetre difference between the nine skittles.

The material used for the skittles was cut from plastic ¾-inch overflow pipe obtained from the local DIY store, with end-stoppers of wood dowelling to accommodate the LED. The reed switch must be as near the top of the skittle as possible so that the swinging magnet can activate it. If the pipe is translucent, the LED can glow inside the skittle. Translucent 35mm film containers can be used as skittles, with LEDs or 6V bulbs as shown in Figure 20.1. The containers are inverted and the bulbs mounted in the lid.

Circuit

The circuits are shown in Figure 20.2 and will be recognised as the familiar flip-flops used in previous games. All flip-flops are identical and are reset by the master reset pushbutton S2 before play. Therefore we need only to consider one circuit. The reset pushbutton switches transistor Tr2 off, which in turn switches off LED D1. Transistor Tr1 is turned on by the base current derived via R3. When the reed switch is actuated by the magnet, Tr1 is switched off and base current is supplied via R1, R2 to Tr2. This transistor switches on and LED D1 lights to indicate a strike. Since a bistable has two stable states, the light stays on until it is reset.

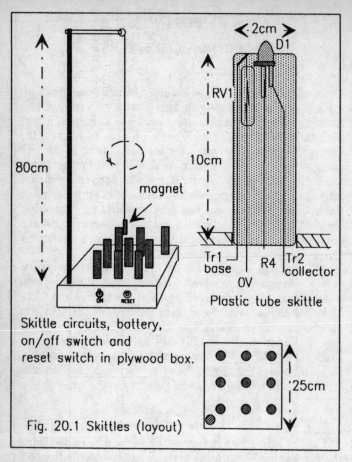

80cm

magnet

Skittle circuits, battery,
on/off switch and
reset switch in plywood box.

←2cm→ D1

RV1

10cm

Tr1 base   R4   Tr2 collector
           0V
Plastic tube skittle

25cm

Fig. 20.1 Skittles (layout)

Components

Nine of each:

Resistors

R1	2.2kΩ
R2	4.7kΩ
R3	4.7kΩ
R4	470Ω (not needed if 6V lamp used)

128

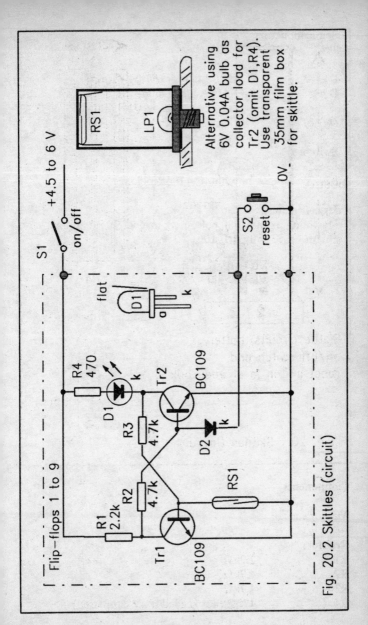

Alternative using 6V 0.04A bulb as collector load for Tr2 (omit D1,R4). Use transparent 35mm film box for skittle.

Fig. 20.2 Skittles (circuit)

Semiconductors

Tr1	BC109
Tr2	BC109
D1	TIL20 LED (or 6V .04A lamp)
D2	1N4148 silicon diode

One of each:

Switches

S1	S.P.S.T.
S2	pushbutton (non-locking)

Miscellaneous

Plywood box material, pole, cord, magnet, plastic tubing, circuit board, wiring, battery.

Please note following is a list of other titles that are available in our range of Radio, Electronics and Computer books.

These should be available from all good Booksellers, Radio Component Dealers and Mail Order Companies.

However, should you experience difficulty in obtaining any title in your area, then please write directly to the Publisher enclosing payment to cover the cost of the book plus adequate postage.

If you would like a complete catalogue of our entire range of Radio, Electronics and Computer Books then please send a Stamped Addressed Envelope to:

BERNARD BABANI (publishing) LTD
THE GRAMPIANS
SHEPHERDS BUSH ROAD
LONDON W6 7NF
ENGLAND